Carol Singer's Handbook

One Hundred Settings
of Traditional Carols
selected & edited by Neil Jenkins

Kevin
Mayhew

We hope you enjoy the music in this book. Further copies are available
from your local music shop or Christian bookshop.

In case of difficulty, please contact the publisher direct by writing to:

The Sales Department
KEVIN MAYHEW LTD
Rattlesden
Bury St Edmunds
Suffolk
IP30 0SZ

Phone 0449 737978
Fax 0449 737834

Please ask for our complete catalogue of outstanding Church Music.

First published in Great Britain in 1993 by Kevin Mayhew Ltd.

ISBN 0 86209 443 7

Front Cover: *Carol Singers* (19th century).
Reproduced by kind permission of Mary Evans Picture Library.
Cover design by Juliette Clarke and Graham Johnstone.

Illustrations taken from engravings by the Dalziel brothers.

Music setting by Kevin Whomes.
Printed and bound in Great Britain.

Contents

Foreword

Carol singing flourished first in the middle ages, and every generation has made its own contribution to the tradition. We are no different today, and like so many others I go 'wassailing' at Christmastime armed with an array of carol books and single sheets of music. Juggling all this music can be an awkward business when you are touring a hospital or nursing home, or singing in the open air. So, in a way, this book is for my own convenience; but I know that it is needed and I hope thousands of others will benefit from having all their favourite carols under one cover.

Carol Singer's Handbook is divided into these easy reference sections:

1. **Wassailing Carols** which are particularly useful for out-of-doors singing.

2. **Lullabies** for quieter moments.

3. **Carols with Refrain** where you will find the jolliest ones.

4. **Traditional Hymns and Carols**

5. **Other Seasons** which includes items suitable for the New Year and other occasions.

For those carols which traditionally have been accompanied by the organ (*Good King Wenceslas* is an example) I have supplied humming parts. These are written for three-part choir and consist of a soprano and bass line with the addition of a third middle part which may be sung by altos or tenors, or both. I hope this will prove to be a practical way of dealing with the inevitable shortage of voices on these lines.

Humming is a particularly effective way of adding variety in the performance of carols. For example, a verse can often be given to a solo voice with the others humming its accompaniment. Occasionally I have suggested how to bring interest to a carol by means of footnotes headed *Performance Suggestions*. I have endeavoured to make *Carol Singer's Handbook* as easy as possible to use by leaving the page uncluttered with editorial markings, and interlining verses for easier sight-reading.

Although *Carol Singer's Handbook* will be of primary interest to groups going out carol-singing who will appreciate its compactness, comprehensiveness and durability, I hope it will also find an additional role in church worship where its straightforward arrangements will make it useful as a Christmas hymnal.

NEIL JENKINS

Acknowledgements

The publishers wish to express their gratitude to the following
for permission to reproduce copyright material.

Bourne Music Ltd, 34/36 Maddox Street, London W1R 9PD, for *Mary's Boy Child*
© Copyright 1956, 1957 by Schumann Music Corp, Hollywood, California/
Bourne Music Ltd for Europe, the British Empire and
Commonwealth of Nations (excl. Canada).

Cassell plc, Villiers House, 41/47 Strand, London WC2N 5JE for
O Christmas Tree (*O Tannenbaum*) and *Echo Carol* (translations).

The Copper Family, Sussex, for their version of *The Twelve Days of Christmas.*

EMI Music Publishing, 127 Charing Cross Road, London WC2H 0EA for
Away in a manger (arrangement), *I saw a maiden sitten and sing* (music),
O babe divine, Sing lullaby (arrangement), *The Angel Gabriel* (arrangement)
and *O little town of Bethlehem* (arrangement) © Copyright B Feldman & Co Ltd,
trading as H Freeman & Co, London WC2H 0EA. Reproduced by permission.

International Music Publications Ltd, Southend Road, Woodford Green,
Essex IG8 8HN for *Little Donkey* © Copyright 1959 Warner Chappell
Music Ltd/International Music Publications Ltd.

The John Ireland Trust, 35 St Mary's Mansions, St Mary's Terrace,
London W2 1SQ for *Adam lay y-bounden* (music).

Magdalene College, Cambridge CB3 0AG for
Whence is that goodly fragrance (translation).

Novello & Co Ltd, 3 Primrose Mews, 1a Sharpleshall Street, London NW1 8YL for
The Twelve Days of Christmas (Frederic Austin Version) and *Adam lay y-bounden* (music).

Oxford University Press, 3 Park Road, London NW1 6XN for the tune *Forest Green*
(*O little town of Bethlehem*) from the *English Hymnal.*

Oxford University Press, Walton Street, Oxford OX2 6DP for
The Rocking Carol (arrangement), *The Cherry Tree Carol* (arrangement) and
When Jesus Christ was yet a child (translation) from *The Oxford Book of Carols.*

Stainer & Bell Ltd, PO Box 110, Victoria House, 23 Gruneisen Road,
London N3 1DZ for *This is the truth* (arrangement).

Every effort has been made to trace the owners of copyright material, and we hope that
no copyright has been infringed. Pardon is sought and apology made if the contrary be
the case, and a correction will be made in any reprint of this book.

Greetings and Wassail Carols

1 CHRISTMAS IS COMING (2-part)

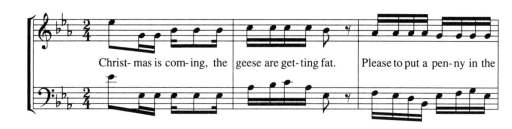

Christ-mas is com-ing, the | geese are get-ting fat. | Please to put a pen-ny in the

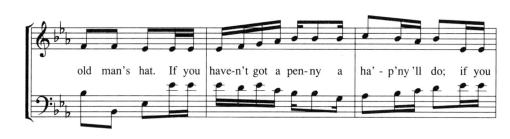

old man's hat. If you | have-n't got a pen-ny a | ha'-p'ny 'll do; if you

have-n't got a ha'-p'ny a | far-thing 'll do; if you | have-n't got a far-thing

*God bless you. God bless the mas-ter

* Optional SATB

of this house, like - wise the mis - tress too, and all the lit - tle

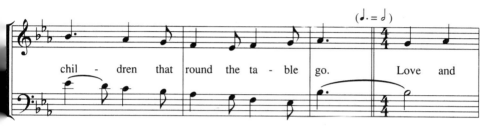

chil - dren that round the ta - ble go. Love and

joy come to you and to you your was - sail too, and God

Love and joy come to you, and to you your was - sail

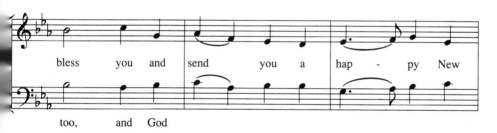

bless you and send you a hap - py New

too, and God

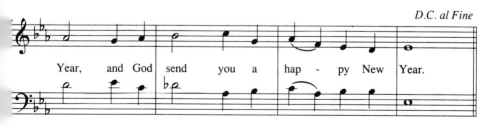

D.C. al Fine

Year, and God send you a hap - py New Year.

Text: Traditional Rhyme
Music: Traditional English Melody arranged Neil Jenkins

9

1a CHRISTMAS IS COMING (4-part)

ha' - p'ny 'll do, a ha' - p'ny 'll do,

but a pen - ny's bet - ter, a

two, three, four! Christ - mas is com - ing, the

pen - ny or two are bet - ter, or three! or four!

geese are get - ting fat, please to put a pen - ny in the old man's hat. If you

fat,

have - n't got a pen - ny a ha' - p'ny 'll do, if you have - n't got a ha' - p'ny, a

far - thing 'll do, if you have - n't got a far - thing,

Text: Traditional Rhyme
Music: Traditional English Melody arranged Henry Walford Davies (1869-1941)

2 COME ALL YOU WORTHY GENTLEMEN

1. Come all you wor - thy gen - tle - men that may be stand - ing by:
2. Christ our bless - ed Sa - viour now in the man - ger lay; He's
3. God bless the ru - ler of this house, and long on may he reign;

Christ our bless - ed Sa - viour was born on Christ - mas day. The
ly - ing in the man - ger, while the o - xen feed on hay. The
ma - ny hap - py Christ - mas - es he live to see a - gain! God

bless - ed Vir - gin Ma - ry un - to the Lord did pray. O we
bless - ed Vir - gin Ma - ry un - to the Lord did pray. O we
bless our ge - ne - ra - tion who live both far and near; and we

wish you the com - fort and ti - dings of joy!
wish you the com - fort and ti - dings of joy!
wish them a hap - py, a hap - py New Year!

* TB in unison with
SA if preferred.

Text: Traditional English collected by Cecil Sharp (1859-1924)
Music: Old English arranged Neil Jenkins

3 DECK THE HALL

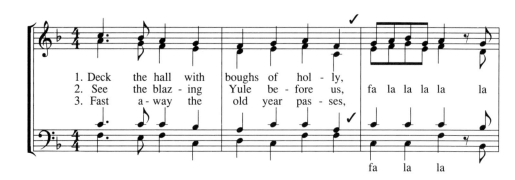

1. Deck the hall with boughs of hol - ly, fa la la la la la
2. See the blaz - ing Yule be - fore us,
3. Fast a - way the old year pas - ses,

fa la la

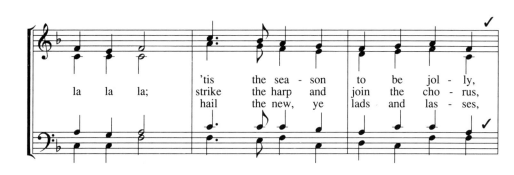

la la la; 'tis the sea - son to be jol - ly,
strike the harp and join the cho - rus,
hail the new, ye lads and las - ses,

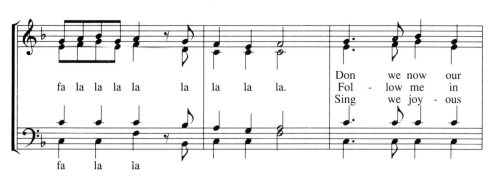

fa la la la la la la la la. Don we now our
Fol - low me in
Sing we joy - ous

fa la la

gay ap - pa - rel,
mer - ry mea - sure,
all to - ge - ther,
fa la la la la la la la la;
fa

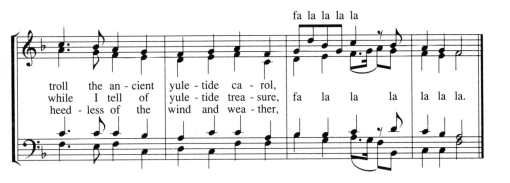

fa la la la la la

troll the an - cient yule - tide ca - rol,
while I tell of yule - tide trea - sure,
heed - less of the wind and wea - ther,
fa la la la la la la.

Text: Traditional (c.1881)
Music: Traditional Welsh Melody arranged Neil Jenkins

4 GOD REST YOU MERRY, GENTLEMEN

Verse

1. God rest you mer - ry, gen - tle - men, let no - thing you dis-
2. In Beth - le - hem, in Jew - ry this bless - ed babe was
3. From God our heav'n - ly Fa - ther, a bless - ed an - gel

may, re - mem - ber Christ our Sa - viour was
born, and laid with - in a man - ger, up -
came, and un - to cer - tain shep - herds, brought

born on Christ - mas day, to save us all from
on this bless - ed morn; the which his mo - ther
ti - dings of the same, how that in Beth - le -

Refrain

Sa - tan's pow'r when we were gone a - stray: O
Ma - ry, did no - thing take in scorn:
hem was born the Son of God by name:

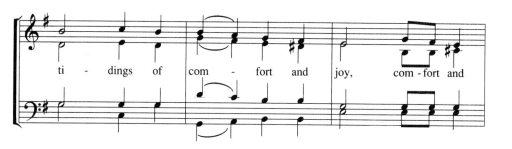

ti - dings of com - fort and joy, com - fort and

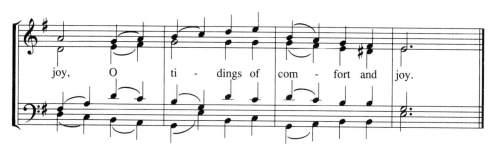

joy, O ti - dings of com - fort and joy.

4. 'Fear not then,' said the angel,
   'let nothing you affright,
   this day is born a Saviour
   of a pure virgin bright,
   to free all those who trust in him
   from Satan's power and might:'
   Refrain

5. The shepherds at those tidings,
   rejoicèd much in mind,
   and left their flocks a-feeding,
   in tempest, storm, and wind:
   and went to Bethlehem straightway,
   the Son of God to find:
   Refrain

6. And when they came to Bethlehem,
   where our dear Saviour lay,
   they found him in a manger,
   where oxen feed on hay;
   his mother Mary kneeling down,
   unto the Lord did pray:
   Refrain

7. Now to the Lord sing praises,
   all you within this place,
   and with true love and brotherhood
   each other now embrace;
   this holy tide of Christmas
   all other doth deface:
   Refrain

Text: Traditional English
Music: Traditional English Melody arranged John Stainer (1840-1901)

5 HERE WE COME A-WASSAILING (2-part)

1. Here we come a - was - sail - ing a -
2. We are not dai - ly beg - gars that
3. Good mas - ter and good mis - tress, as

mong the leaves so green, here we come a -
beg from door to door, but we are friends and
you sit by the fire, but pray think of us poor

wan - der - ing so fair to be seen.
neigh - bours whom you have seen be - fore. Love and
chil - dren who wan - der in the mire.

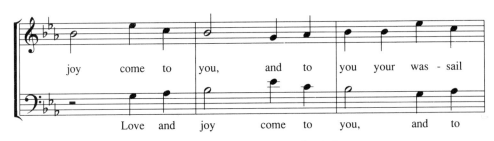

joy come to you, and to you your was - sail
Love and joy come to you, and to

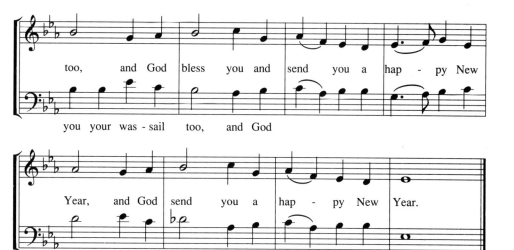

too, and God bless you and send you a hap - py New

you your was - sail too, and God

Year, and God send you a hap - py New Year.

4. / We have got a little purse
   of softest leather skin;
   we want some of your small change
   to line it well within.
   Refrain

5. Call / up the butler of this house,
   put / on his golden ring;
   let him / bring us up a glass of beer,
   and better we shall sing.
   Refrain

6. Now / bring us out a table,
   and spread it with a cloth;
   and / bring us out a / mouldy cheese,
   and / some of your Christmas / loaf.
   Refrain

7. God / bless the master / of this house,
   like / wise the mistress / too;
   and all the little children
   that round the table go.
   Refrain

8. And / all your kin and kinsfolk,
   that dwell both far and near;
   we / wish a merry / Christmas,
   and a / happy New Year.
   Refrain

Performance Suggestion:
Verse 1 Full, unison top part only
Verse 2 Full, 2-part
Verses 3,4 SA solo
Verses 5,6 TB solo
Verses 7,8 Full, 2-part

Omit Verses 5,6 if desired

Text: Traditional
Music: Traditional English Melody arranged Neil Jenkins

5a HERE WE COME A-WASSAILING (4-part)

The lyrics beneath the music:

too, and God bless you and send you a hap - py New Year, and God send you a hap - py New Year.

4. / We have got a little purse
   of softest leather skin;
   we want some of your small change
   to line it well within.
   Refrain

* 5. Call / up the butler of this house,
   put / on his golden ring;
   let him / bring us up a glass of beer,
   and better we shall sing.
   Refrain

* 6. Now / bring us out a table,
   and spread it with a cloth;
   and / bring us out a / mouldy cheese,
   and / some of your Christmas / loaf.
   Refrain

7. God / bless the master / of this house,
   like / wise the mistress / too;
   and all the little children
   that round the table go.
   Refrain

8. And / all your kin and kinsfolk,
   that dwell both far and near;
   we / wish a merry / Christmas,
   and a / happy New Year.
   Refrain

* Omit if desired.

Text: Traditional
Music: Traditional English Melody arranged John Stainer (1840-1901)

6 JOY TO THE WORLD

1. Joy to the world! the Lord is
2. Joy to the world! the Sa - viour
3. He rules the world with truth and

come: let earth re - ceive her king.
reigns; let men their songs em - ploy;
grace, and makes the na - tions prove,

Let eve - ry heart pre - pare him
while fields and floods, rocks, hills, and
the glo - ries of his right - eous -

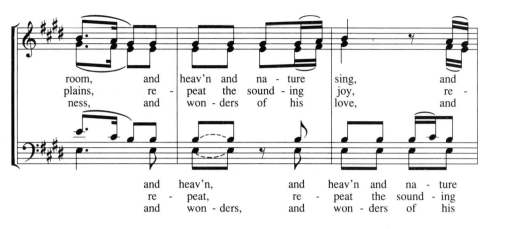

room, and heav'n and na - ture sing, and
plains, re - peat the sound - ing joy, re -
ness, and won - ders of his love, and

and heav'n, and heav'n and na - ture
re - peat, re - peat the sound - ing
and won - ders, and won - ders of his

heav'n and na - ture sing, and heav'n and
peat the sound - ing joy, re - peat, re -
won - ders of his love, and won - ders,

sing, and heav'n and na - ture sing, and
joy, re - peat the sound - ing joy, re -
love, and won - ders of his love, and

heav'n and na - ture sing.
peat the sound - ing joy.
won - ders of his love.

Text: Isaac Watts (1674-1748)
Music: 'Antioch' arranged Lowell Mason (1792-1872) and Neil Jenkins

7 LISTEN, LORDINGS, UNTO ME

Verse

1. Lis - ten, lord - ings, un - to me, a tale I will you tell;
2. In the inn they found no room; a scan - ty bed they made:
3. Shep - herds lay a - field that night to keep the sil - ly sheep,
4. On - ward then the an - gels sped, the shep - herds on - ward went,

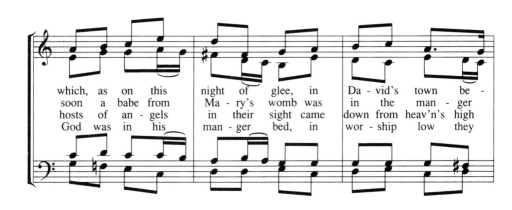

which, as on this night of glee, in Da - vid's town be -
soon a babe from Ma - ry's womb was in the man - ger
hosts of an - gels in their sight came down from heav'n's high
God was in his man - ger bed, in wor - ship low they

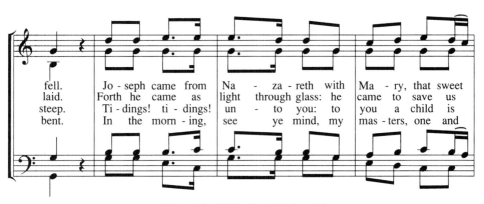

fell. Jo - seph came from Na - za - reth with Ma - ry, that sweet
laid. Forth he came as light through glass: he came to save us
steep. Ti - dings! ti - dings! un - to you: to you a child is
bent. In the morn - ing, see ye mind, my mas - ters, one and

Text: Henry Ramsden Bramley (1833-1917)
Music: Frederick Arthur Gore Ouseley (1825-1889)

8 O CHRISTMAS TREE

boughs so green in sum - mer - time, do
lit - tle stars, your can - dles bright, send

brave the snow of win - ter time. O Christ - mas tree, O
to the world a won - drous light. O Christ - mas tree, O

Christ - mas tree, O tree of green un - chang - ing.
Christ - mas tree, you set my heart a - sing - ing.

3. O Christmas tree, O Christmas tree,
   you come from God, eternal. *(Repeat)*
   A symbol of the Lord of love,
   whom God to man sent from above.
   O Christmas tree, O Christmas tree,
   you come from God, eternal.

4. O Christmas tree, O Christmas tree,
   you speak of God, unchanging. *(Repeat)*
   You tell us all to faithful be,
   and trust in God eternally.
   O Christmas tree, O Christmas tree,
   you speak of God, unchanging.

Text: Ernst Anschütz translated by Ruth Heller
Music: German Melody arranged Neil Jenkins

9 PAST THREE O'CLOCK

Refrain

Past three o' - clock, and a cold fro - sty morn - ing:

past three o' - clock; good mor - row, mas - ters all!

4. Hinds o'er the pearly
   dewy lawn early
   seek the high stranger
   laid in the manger.
   Refrain

5. Light out of star-land
   leadeth from far land
   princes, to meet him,
   worship and greet him.
   Refrain

6. Myrrh from full coffer,
   incense they offer:
   nor is the golden
   treasure withholden.
   Refrain

7. Thus they: I pray you,
   up, sirs, nor stay you
   till ye confess him
   likewise, and bless him.
   Refrain

Text: George Ratcliffe Woodward (1848-1934)
Music: Traditional English Melody arranged Charles Wood (1866-1926)

10 THE BOAR'S HEAD CAROL

Solo

1. The boar's head in hand bear I, be-
2. The boar's head, as I un - der - stand is the
3. Our ste - ward hath pro - vi - ded this in

decked with bays and rose - ma - ry; and I pray you my mas - ters
bra - vest dish in all the land when thus be - decked with a
hon - our of the king of bliss which on this day to be

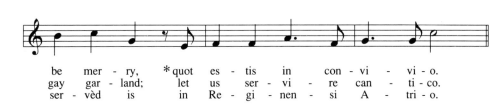

be mer - ry, *quot es - tis in con - vi - vi - o.
gay gar - land; let us ser - vi - re can - ti - co.
ser - vèd is in Re - gi - nen - si A - tri - o.

1st Refrain (Verses 1, 2)

D.C.

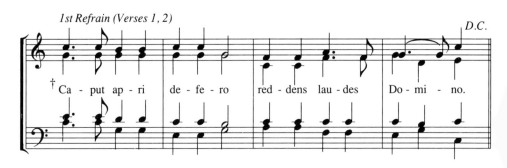

†Ca - put ap - ri de - fe - ro red - dens lau - des Do - mi - no.

2nd Refrain (Verse 3)

Ca - put ap - ri | de - fe - ro | red - dens lau - des | Do - mi - no,

lau - des Do - min - o, | lau - des Do - mi - no, | Do - mi - no.

* *Translation:* Verse 1   as many as are at the feast.
      Verse 2   serve it with a song.
      Verse 3   in Queen's Hall.

† *Translation:*   I bring in the boar's head, giving thanks to the Lord.

Text: Wynkyn de Worde's *Christmas Carols* (1521)
Music: Traditional English

11 THE MUMMER'S SONG

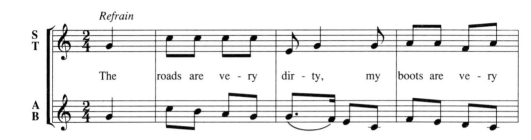

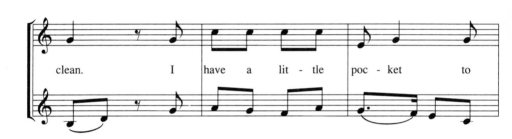

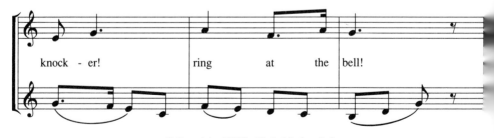

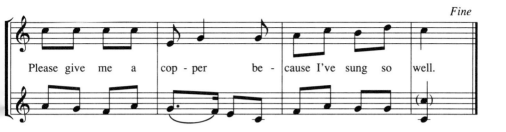

Fine

Please give me a cop-per be-cause I've sung so well.

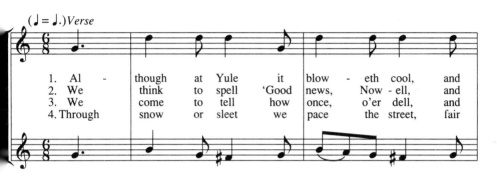

(♩ = ♩.) *Verse*

1. Al - though at Yule it blow - eth cool, and
2. We think to spell 'Good news, Now - ell, and
3. We come to tell how once, o'er dell, and
4. Through snow or sleet we pace the street, fair

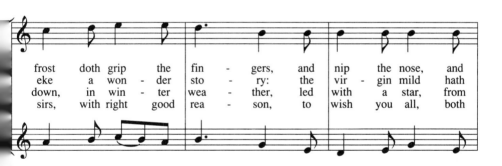

frost doth grip the fin - gers, and nip the nose, and
eke a won - der sto - ry: the vir - gin mild hath
down, in win - ter wea - ther, led with a star, from
sirs, with right good rea - son, to wish you all, both

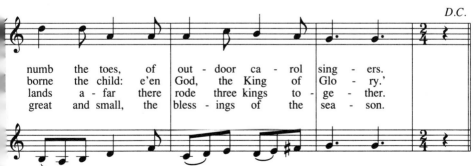

D.C.

numb the toes, of out - door ca - rol sing - ers.
borne the child: e'en God, the King of Glo - ry.'
lands a - far there rode three kings to - ge - ther.
great and small, the bless - ings of the sea - son.

Text: George Ratcliffe Woodward (1848-1934) and Traditional English Rhyme
Music: Traditional German & English Melodies arranged Charles Wood (1866-1926) & Neil Jenkins

12 THE TWELVE DAYS OF CHRISTMAS (2-part)

1. On the first day of Christ - mas my true love sent to me a

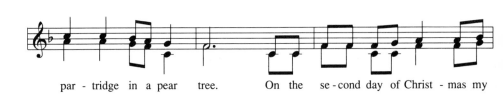

par - tridge in a pear tree. On the se - cond day of Christ - mas my

true love sent to me two tur - tle doves and a par - tridge in a pear tree.

Verse 4 only

On the third / fourth day of Christ - mas my true love sent to me four ca - na - ry birds,

three French hens, two tur - tle doves and a par - tridge in a pear tree.

Music: Reproduced by kind permission of the Copper family.

It is illegal to photocopy music.

On the fifth day of Christ - mas my true love sent to me

five gold rings, four ca - na - ry birds, three French hens,

two tur - tle doves and a par - tridge in a pear tree. On the

Repeat as necessary

sixth	day of Christ - mas my true love sent to me
seventh	
eighth	
ninth	
tenth	
eleventh	
twelfth	

six	geese	a - lay - ing,
seven	swans	a - swim - ming,
eight	deers	a - run - ning,
nine	lads	a - leap - ing,
ten	lad - ies	skip - ping,
eleven	bears	a - bait - ing,
twelve	par - sons	preach - ing,

five gold rings, four ca - na - ry birds,

three French hens, two tur - tle doves and a par - tridge in a pear tree.

Text: Traditional English
Music: Traditional English (Copper Family Version)

13 THE TWELVE DAYS OF CHRISTMAS (4-part)

1. On the first day of Christ-mas my true love sent to me a par-tridge in a pear tree. 2. On the sec-ond day of Christ-mas my true love sent to me two tur-tle doves and a par-tridge in a pear tree. 3. 4. On the third fourth day of Christ-mas my true love sent to me

Verse 4 only

four cal - ling birds, three French hens, two tur - tle doves and a

par - tridge in a pear tree. 5. On the fifth day of Christ - mas my

true love sent to me five gold rings,

four cal - ling birds, three French hens, two tur - tle doves and a

Text: Traditional English Rhyme
Music: Traditional English Melody arranged Neil Jenkins

14 THE WAITS' SONG

The moon shines bright and the stars give a light a
A - wake, a - wake, good peo - ple all, a -
O fair, O fair Je - ru - sa - lem, when

lit - tle be - fore the day: our migh - ty Lord he
wake, and you shall hear, the Lord our God died
shall I come to thee? When shall my sor - rows

looked on us, and bade us a - wake and pray.
on the cross for us he loved so dear.
have an end, thy joy that I may see?

4. The fields were green as green could be,
   when from his glorious seat,
   our blessed Father watered us,
   with his / heavenly dew so sweet.

5. And for the saving of our souls
   Christ died upon the cross;
   we ne'er shall do for Jesus Christ
   as he hath done for us.

6. The life of man is but a span,
   and cut down in its flower;
   we're here today, tomorrow gone,
   the creatures of an hour.

7. My song is done, I must be gone,
   I can / stay no longer here;
   God bless you all, both great and small,
   and / send you a joyful New / Year.

Text: Traditional English
Music: Traditional English Melody arranged John Stainer (1840-1901)

15 THIS IS THE TRUTH (2 or 3-part)

Solo or unison

This is the truth sent from a-bove, the truth of God, the

God of love, there-fore don't turn me from your door,

but hear-ken all both rich and poor.

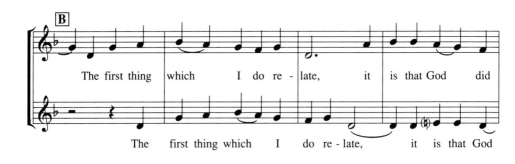

The first thing which I do re-late, it is that God did

The first thing which I do re-late, it is that God

man cre-ate; the next thing which to you I'll tell:

did man cre-ate; the next thing which to you I'll

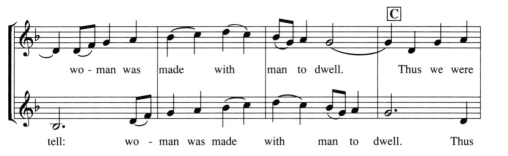

wo - man was made with man to dwell. Thus we were

tell: wo - man was made with man to dwell. Thus

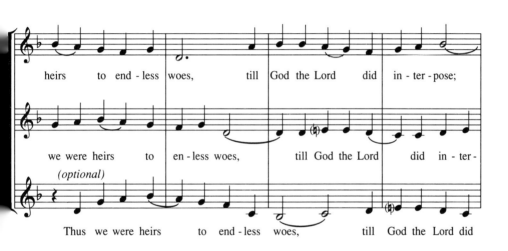

heirs to end - less woes, till God the Lord did in - ter - pose;

we were heirs to en - less woes, till God the Lord did in - ter -

(optional)

Thus we were heirs to end - less woes, till God the Lord did

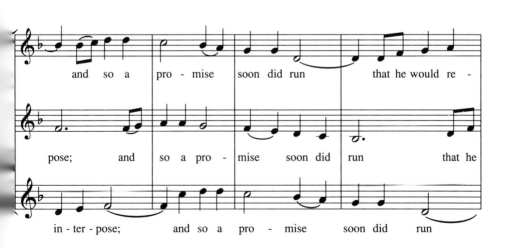

and so a pro - mise soon did run that he would re -

pose; and so a pro - mise soon did run that he

in - ter - pose; and so a pro - mise soon did run

* Voices 2 and 3 can continue singing their parts in the manner of a round.

Text: Traditional English
Music: Traditional English Melody arranged Neil Jenkins

15a THIS IS THE TRUTH (4-Part)

1. This is the truth sent from a - bove, the
2. The first thing which I do re - late
3. Thus we were heirs to end - less woes, till

truth of God, the God of love; there - fore don't turn me
is that God did man cre - ate; the next thing which to
God the Lord did in - ter - pose; and so a pro - mise

from your door, but hear - ken all both rich and poor.
you I'll tell: wo - man was made with man to dwell.
soon did run that he would re - deem us by his son.

4. And at that season of the year
   our / blest Redeemer did appear;
   he here did live, and here did preach,
   and / many thousands he did teach.

5. Thus he in love to us behaved,
   to / show us how we must be saved;
   and if you want to know the way,
   be / pleased to hear what he did say.

6. God grant to all within this place
   true / saving faith, that special grace
   which to his people doth belong:
   and / thus I close my Christmas song.

Text: Traditional English
Music: Traditional English arranged Ralph Vaughan Williams (1872-1958)

16 WASSAIL ALL OVER THE TOWN

1. Was - sail,* was - sail all o - ver the town! Our toast it is white and our ale it is brown, our bowl it is made of the white ma - ple tree; with the

2. And here's to Dob - bin and to his right eye, pray God send our mas - ter a good Christ - mas pie, and a good Christ - mas pie that may we all see; with our

3. And here's to Fill - pail and to her left ear, pray God send our mas - ter a hap - py New Year, and a hap - py New Year as e'er he did see; with our

* Wes hal (old English) meaning 'Be thou hale'.

was - sail - ing | bowl we'll | drink to | thee.

4. Come, / butler, come / fill us a / bowl of the / best,
then we / hope that your / soul in / heaven may / rest;
but / if you do / draw us a / bowl of the / small,
then / down shall go / butler, / bowl and / all.

5. Then / here's to the / maid in the / lily white / smock,
who / tripped to the / door and / slipped back the / lock!
who / tripped to the / door and / pulled back the / pin,
for to / let these / jolly / wassailers / in.

6. Then / here's to the / master, the / mistress al / so,
and / all of the / children that / round them do / go;
and / all of their / kin, both / far and / near,
these / wassailers / wish a / happy New / Year.

Performance Suggestion:
Verse 1 Full
Verse 2 Solo TB
Verse 3 Solo SA
Verse 4 Full TB
Verse 5 Full SA
Verse 6 Full

Text: Traditional
Music: Traditional arranged Neil Jenkins

17 WE WISH YOU A MERRY CHRISTMAS

Verse

1. We wish you a mer-ry Christ-mas, we wish you a mer-ry

Christ-mas, we wish you a mer-ry Christ-mas and a hap-py New

Refrain

Year. Good ti-dings we bring to

you and your kin. We wish you a mer-ry Christ-mas and a

*3. **For we all like** figgy **pudding**,
   we **all like** figgy **pudding**,
   we **all like** figgy **pudding**,
   so bring some out here.

4. **And we won't go** until we've **got some**,
   we **won't go** until we've **got some**,
   we **won't go** until we've **got some**,
   so bring some out here.

* The words for AB in verses 3 and 4 are in bold type.

Text: Traditional English
Music: Traditional English arranged Neil Jenkins

Lullabies

18 AWAY IN A MANGER (1)

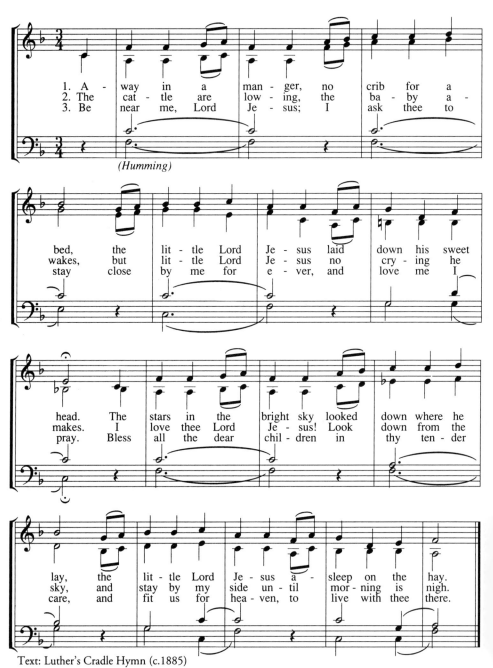

(Humming)

1. A - way in a man - ger, no crib for a bed, the lit - tle Lord Je - sus laid down his sweet head. The stars in the bright sky looked down where he lay, the lit - tle Lord Je - sus a - sleep on the hay.

2. The cat - tle are low - ing, the ba - by a - wakes, but lit - tle Lord Je - sus no cry - ing he makes. I love thee Lord Je - sus! Look down from the sky, and stay by my side un - til mor - ning is nigh.

3. Be near me, Lord Je - sus; I ask thee to stay close by me for e - ver, and love me I pray. Bless all the dear chil - dren in thy ten - der care, and fit us for hea - ven, to live with thee there.

Text: Luther's Cradle Hymn (c.1885)
Music: William James Kirkpatrick (1838-1921) arranged Neil Jenkins

18a AWAY IN A MANGER (2)

1. A - way in a man - ger, no crib for a bed, the lit - tle Lord Je - sus laid down his sweet head. The stars in the bright sky looked down where he lay, the lit - tle Lord Je - sus a - sleep on the hay.

2. The cat - tle are low - ing, the ba - by a - wakes, but lit - tle Lord Je - sus no cry - ing he makes. I love thee Lord Je - sus! Look down from the sky, and stay by my side un - til mor - ning is nigh.

3. Be near me, Lord Je - sus; I ask thee to stay close by me for e - ver, and love me I pray. Bless all the dear chil - dren in thy ten - der care, and fit us for hea - ven, to live with thee there.

Text: Luther's Cradle Hymn (c.1885)
Music: William James Kirkpatrick (1838-1921) arranged Neil Jenkins

19 AWAY IN A MANGER (3)

1. A - way in a man - ger, no crib for a bed, the lit - tle Lord Je - sus laid down his sweet head. The stars in the bright sky looked down where he lay, the lit - tle Lord Je - sus a - sleep on the hay.

2. The cat - tle are low - ing, the ba - by a - wakes, but lit - tle Lord Je - sus no cry - ing he makes. I love thee Lord Je - sus! Look down from the sky, and stay by my side un - til mor - ning is nigh.

3. Be near me, Lord Je - sus; I ask thee to stay close by me for e - ver, and love me I pray. Bless all the dear chil - dren in thy ten - der care, and fit us for hea - ven, to live with thee there.

Text: Luther's Cradle Hymn (c.1885)
Music: Normandy Carol arranged Edgar Pettman (1865-1943)
Music: © Copyright 1920 B. Feldman & Co Ltd, trading as H. Freeman & Co, London WC2H OEA.
It is illegal to photocopy music.

20 CHILD IN THE MANGER

1. Child in the man - ger, in - fant of Ma - ry;
2. Once the most ho - ly child of sal - va - tion,
3. Pro - phets fore - told him, in - fant of won - der;

out - cast and stran - ger, Lord of all!
gent - ly and low - ly, lived be - low;
an - gels be - hold him on his throne;

Child who in - he - rits all our trans - gres - sions,
now, as our glo - rious migh - ty Re - deem - er,
wor - thy our Sa - viour of all their prais - es;

all our de - mer - its on him fall.
see him vic - to - rious o'er each foe.
hap - py for e - ver are his own.

Text: Mary Macdonald (1817-1890) translated by Lachlan Macbean (1853-1931)
Music: Traditional Gaelic Melody arranged Neil Jenkins

21 INFANT HOLY, INFANT LOWLY

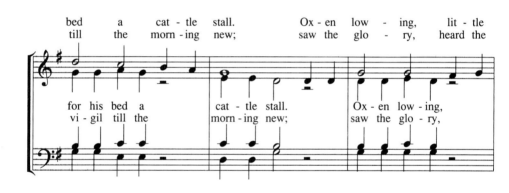

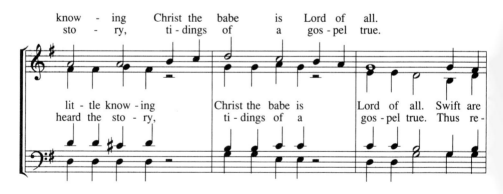

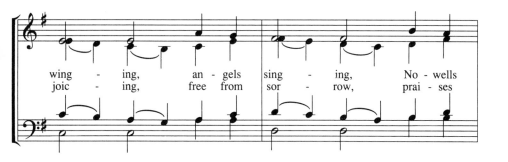

wing - ing, an - gels sing - ing, No - wells
joic - ing, free from sor - row, prai - ses

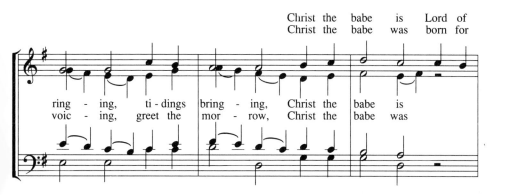

Christ the babe is Lord of
Christ the babe was born for

ring - ing, ti - dings bring - ing, Christ the babe is
voic - ing, greet the mor - row, Christ the babe was

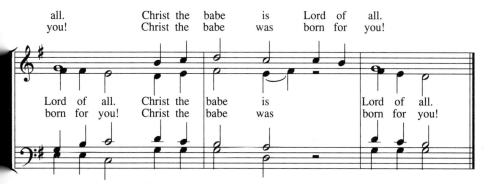

all. Christ the babe is Lord of all.
you! Christ the babe was born for you!

Lord of all. Christ the babe is Lord of all.
born for you! Christ the babe was born for you!

Text: Polish Carol translated by Edith Margaret Reed (1885-1933)
Music: Traditional Polish arranged Neil Jenkins

22 I SAW A FAIR MAIDEN

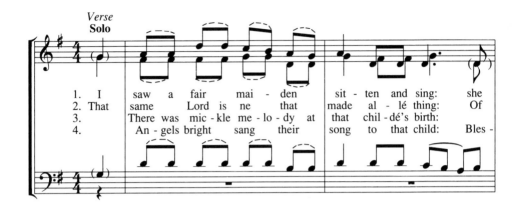

Verse
Solo

1. I saw a fair mai - den sit - ten and sing: she
2. That same Lord is ne that made al - lé thing: Of
3. There was mic - kle me - lo - dy at that chil - dé's birth:
4. An - gels bright sang their song to that child: Bles -

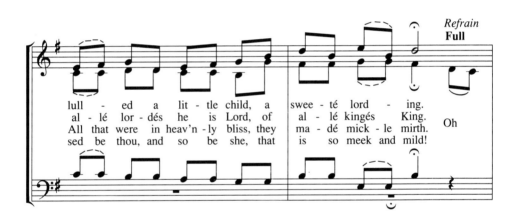

Refrain
Full

lull - ed a lit - tle child, a swee - té lord - ing.
al - lé lor - dés he is Lord, of al - lé kingés King. Oh
All that were in heav'n - ly bliss, they ma - dé mick - le mirth.
sed be thou, and so be she, that is so meek and mild!

Lul - lay my lik - ing, my dear son, my sweet - ing,

Lul - la - lay, lul - la - lay

Lul - la - lay, lul - la - lay,

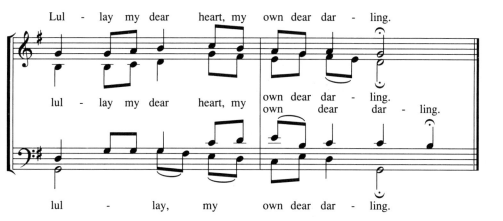

Text: From the *Sloane* Manuscript (c.15th century)
Music: Richard Runciman Terry (1865-1938) adapted Neil Jenkins

23 I SAW A MAIDEN SITTEN AND SING

1. I saw a mai-den sit-ten and sing: she lull'd her child, a lit-tle lord-ing.
2. This ve-ry Lord, he made all things, and this ve-ry God, the King of all kings.
3. There was sweet mu-sic at this child's birth, and heav'n filled with an-gels, ma-king much mirth.

Lul - lay, lul - lay, my dear son, my sweet - ing; lul - lay, lul - lay, my dear son, my own dear dar - ling.

4. Heav'n's angels sang to / welcome the child
   now / born of a maid, all / undefiled.

5. Pray we and sing on / this festal day
   that / peace may dwell with / us alway.

Text: From the *Sloane* Manuscript (c.15th century)
Music: Edgar Pettman (1865-1943)

24 I SING OF A MAIDEN

Text: Traditional (15th century)
Music: Richard Runciman Terry (1865-1938)

25 LULLAY MY LIKING

Refrain

Lul - lay my lik - ing, my dear son, my sweet - ing;
lul - lay my dear heart, mine own dear dar - ling!

Verse
Solo

1. I saw a fair mai - den sit - ten and sing: she
lul - led a lit - tle child, a swee - té lord - ing,

to Refrain

Verse
Solo

2. That e - ter - nal Lord is he that made al - le thing; of
al - le lord - es he is Lord, of al - le king - es King.

to Refrain

3. There was mick-le me-lo-dy at that child-es birth: al-though they were in hea-ven's bliss they ma-de mick-le mirth.

to Refrain

Verse
Full

4. An-gels bright, they sang that night and said-en to that child, bless-ed be thou, and so be she, that is both meek and mild.'

to Refrain

Verse
Solo

5. Pray we now to that child, and to his mo-ther dear, God grant them all his bless-ing that now ma-ken cheer.

to Refrain

Text: From the *Sloane* Manuscript (c.15th century)
Music: Gustav Holst (1874-1934)

26 O BABE DIVINE

Slowly and softly

1. O babe di - vine, now will I sing to thee a song of love - long - ing: make in my heart a quick well spring, thy - self to love a - bove all thing.

mf <

mf <

molto rit.

2. O holy child, my dim heart's gleam,
   O brighter than the sunny beam!
   As thou wast born in Bethlehem,
   be born in me and be my dream.

3. O prince of peace, my dark soul's light!
   Thou art a day without a night:
   O give me strength and give me might
   ever to love thyself aright.

4. Jesu, it well for him shall be
   that in thy bliss thyself shall see:
   O then with love-chords draw thou me,
   that I may come and dwell with thee.

Text: Old English adapted by William Adair Pickard-Cambridge (1879-1957)
Music: Edgar Pettman (1865-1943)

27 O LITTLE ONE SWEET

1. O lit - tle one sweet, O
2. O lit - tle one sweet, O
3. O lit - tle one sweet, O
4. O lit - tle one sweet, O

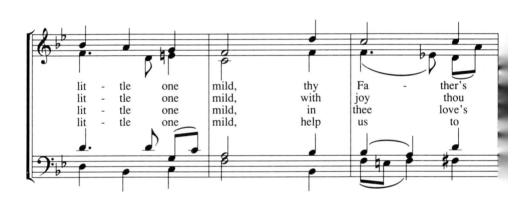

lit - tle one mild, thy Fa - ther's
lit - tle one mild, with joy thou
lit - tle one mild, in thee love's
lit - tle one mild, help us to

pur - pose thou hast ful - filled; thou
hast the whole world filled; thou
beau - ties are all dis - tilled; then
do as thou hast willed. Lo,

cam'st   from   heav'n   to   mor -   tal
cam -   est   here   from   heav'n's   do -
light   in   us   thy   love's   bright
all   we   have   be -   longs   to

ken,   e -   qual   to   be   with
main   to   bring   men   com -   fort
flame,   that   we   may   give   thee
thee!   Ah,   keep   us   in   our

us   poor   men,
in   their   pain,   O   lit -   tle   one
back   the   same,
fe -   al -   ty!

sweet,   O   lit -   tle   one   mild.

Text: Samuel Scheidt (1587-1654) translated by Percy Dearmer (1867-1936)
Music: German Melody harmonised by Johann Sebastian Bach (1685-1750)

28 O SLEEP, THOU HEAV'N-BORN TREASURE

Text: Traditional German translated by Arthur Foxton Ferguson
Music: Attributed Carl Neuner (1814) arranged Charles Macpherson (1870-1927) adapted Neil Jenkins

29 SILENT NIGHT (1)

(Humming)

1. Si - lent night! Ho - ly night!
2. Si - lent night! Ho - ly night!
3. Si - lent night! Ho - ly night!

All is calm, all is bright, round yon vir - gin
Shep - herds quail at the sight; glo - ries stream from
Son of God, love's pure light; rad - iant beams thy

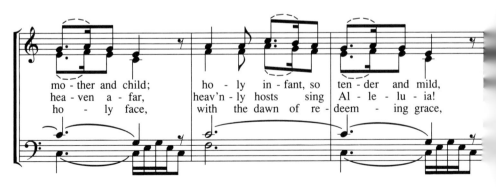

mo - ther and child; ho - ly in - fant, so ten - der and mild,
hea - ven a - far, heav'n - ly hosts sing Al - le - lu - ia!
ho - ly face, with the dawn of re - deem - ing grace,

sleep in hea - ven - ly peace, sleep in hea - ven - ly
Christ the Sa - viour is born, Christ the Sa - viour is
Je - sus, Lord, at thy birth, Je - sus Lord, at thy

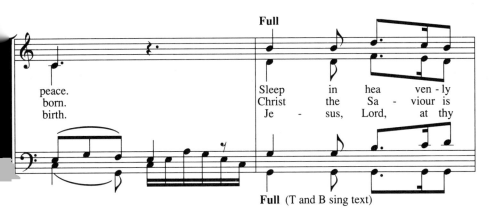

Full

peace.   Sleep in hea ven - ly
born.   Christ the Sa - viour is
birth.   Je - sus, Lord, at thy

Full (T and B sing text)

peace,   sleep in hea - ven - ly peace.
born,   Christ the Sa - viour is born.
birth,   Je - sus, Lord, at thy birth.

Text: Joseph Möhr (1792-1848) translated by John Freeman Young (1820-1885)
Music: Franz Grüber (1787-1863) arranged Neil Jenkins

29a SILENT NIGHT (2)

1. Si - lent night! Ho - ly night!
2. Si - lent night! Ho - ly night!
3. Si - lent night! Ho - ly night!

All is calm, all is bright, round yon vir - gin
Shep - herds quail at the sight; glo - ries stream from
Son of God, love's pure light; ra - diant beams thy

mo - ther and child; ho - ly in - fant so
hea - ven a - far, heav'n - ly hosts sing
ho - ly face, with the dawn of re -

ten - der and mild,   sleep   in   hea - ven - ly
Al - le - lu - ia!   Christ   the   Sa - viour is
deem - ing grace,   Je - sus, Lord, at thy

Optional repeat

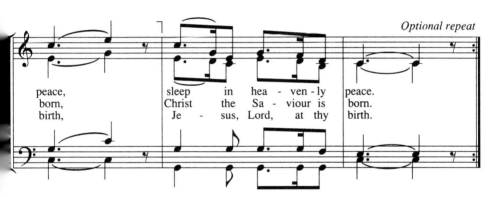

peace,   sleep in hea - ven - ly peace.
born,   Christ the Sa - viour is born.
birth,   Je - sus, Lord, at thy birth.

* Alternative (original melody)

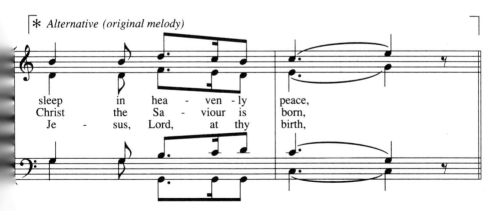

sleep   in   hea - ven - ly peace,
Christ   the   Sa - viour is born,
Je - sus, Lord, at thy birth,

Performance Suggestion: Verses 1, 2: original version (No. 29)
                          Verse 3: 4-part version (No. 29a) with repeat of last 4 bars.

Text: Joseph Möhr (1792-1848) translated by John Freeman Young (1820-1885)
Music: Franz Grüber (1787-1863) arranged Neil Jenkins

30 SING LULLABY

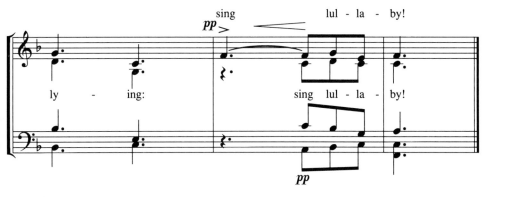

2. Sing lullaby!
   Lullaby baby, now a-sleeping,
   sing lullaby!
   Hush, do not wake the infant king,
   soon will come sorrow with the morning,
   soon will come bitter grief and weeping:
   sing lullaby!

3. Sing lullaby!
   Lullaby baby, now a-dozing,
   sing lullaby!
   Hush, do not wake the infant king,
   soon comes the cross, the nails, the piercing,
   then in the grave at last reposing:
   sing lullaby!

4. Sing lullaby!
   Lullaby! is the babe a-waking?
   sing lullaby!
   Hush, do not stir the infant king.
   Dreaming of Easter, gladsome morning,
   conquering death, its bondage breaking:
   sing lullaby!

Text: Sabine Baring-Gould (1834-1924)
Music: Basque Noël arranged Edgar Pettman (1865-1943)

31 SLEEP! HOLY BABE

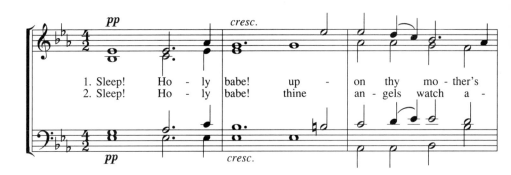

1. Sleep! Ho - ly babe! up - on thy mo - ther's
2. Sleep! Ho - ly babe! thine an - gels watch a -

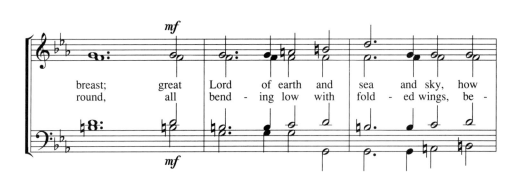

breast; great Lord of earth and sea and sky, how
round, all bend - ing low with fold - ed wings, be -

sweet it is to see thee lie in
fore the in - car - nate King of kings, in

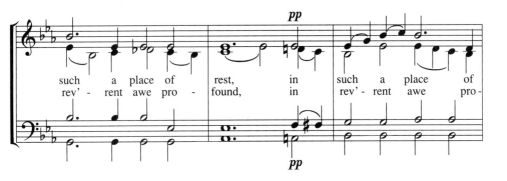

such   a   place   of   rest,   in   such   a   place   of
rev' -   rent awe   pro -   found,   in   rev' -   rent awe   pro -

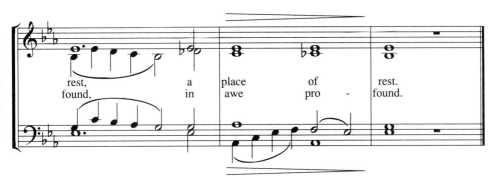

rest,   a   place   of   rest.
found,   in   awe   pro -   found.

3. Sleep! Holy babe! while I with Mary gaze
   in joy upon that face awhile,
   upon the loving infant smile
   which there divinely plays,
   which there divinely plays,
   divinely plays.

4. Sleep! Holy babe! Ah! take thy brief repose;
   too quickly will thy slumbers break,
   and thou to lengthened pains awake
   that death alone shall close,
   that death alone shall close,
   alone shall close.

Text: Edward Caswall (1814-1878)
Music: John Bacchus Dykes (1823-1876) arranged Neil Jenkins

32 SWEET WAS THE SONG THE VIRGIN SUNG

Text: William Ballet's Lute Book (c.1590)
Music: English Lute-song arranged Thomas Hamond (*d*.1662)

33 THE ROCKING CAROL

1. Lit - tle Je - sus, sweet - ly sleep, do not stir; we will lend a coat of fur, we will rock you, rock you, rock you, we will rock you, rock you, rock you: see the fur to keep you warm, snug - ly round your ti - ny form.

2. Ma - ry's lit - tle ba - by sleep, sweet - ly sleep, sleep in com - fort, slum - ber deep; we will rock you, rock you, rock you, we will rock you, rock you, rock you: we will serve you all we can, dar - ling, dar - ling lit - tle man.

Text: Czech Carol translated by Percy Dearmer (1867-1936)
Music: Traditional Czech arranged Martin Shaw (1875-1958)

Carols with Refrain

34 A CHILD THIS DAY IS BORN

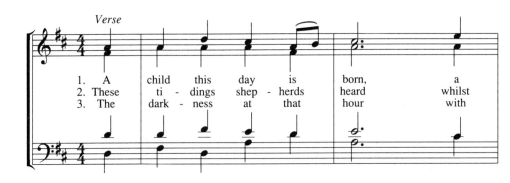

Verse

1. A child this day is born, a
2. These ti - dings shep - herds heard whilst
3. The dark - ness at that hour with

child of high re - nown; most wor - thy of a
watch - ing o'er their fold, 'twas by an an - gel
glo - rious light was rent; a heav'n - ly host of

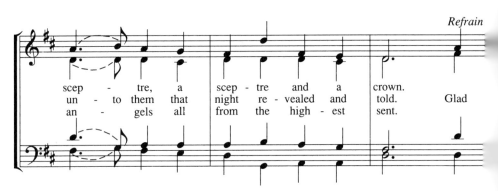

Refrain

scep - tre, a scep - tre and a crown. Glad
un - to them that night re - vealed and told.
an - gels all from the high - est sent.

ti - dings to all men, glad ti - dings sing we may, be -

cause the King of all kings was born on Christ - mas day.

4. They praised the Lord our God
   and our celestial king.
   All glory be in paradise,
   this heavenly host do sing.
   Refrain

5. All glory be to God,
   that sitteth still on high,
   with praises and with triumph great,
   and joyful melody.
   Refrain

Text: Taken from William Sandys' *Christmas Carols, Ancient and Modern* (1833)
Music: Traditional English Melody arranged John Stainer (1840-1901)

35 A GREAT AND MIGHTY WONDER

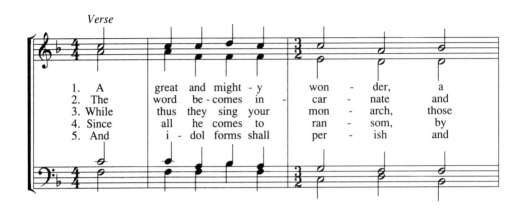

Verse

1. A great and might - y won - der, a
2. The word be - comes in - car - nate and
3. While thus they sing your mon - arch, those
4. Since all he comes to ran - som, by
5. And i - dol forms shall per - ish and

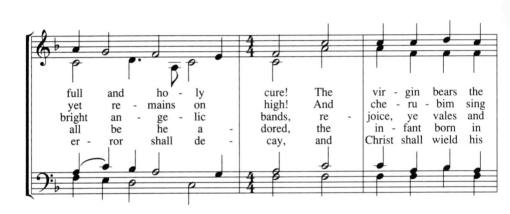

full and ho - ly cure! The vir - gin bears the
yet re - mains on high! And che - ru - bim sing
bright an - ge - lic bands, re - joice, ye vales and
all be he a - dored, the in - fant born in
er - ror shall de - cay, and Christ shall wield his

Refrain

in - fant with vir - gin hon - our pure.
an - thems to shep - herds from the sky.
moun - tains, ye o - ceans clap your hands. Re -
Beth - lem, the Sa - viour and the Lord.
scep - tre, our Lord and God for aye.

peat the hymn a - gain!   'To God on high be

peace on   earth   to   men!'

glo - ry,   and   peace on   earth   to   men!'
                     peace on earth   to   men!'

Text: St. Germanus (634-732) translated by John Mason Neale (1818-1866)
Music: German Melody harmonised by Michael Praetorius (1571-1621)

Alternative Text:

35a THE NOBLE STEM OF JESSE

1. The noble stem of Jesse
   hath flow'red at this tide:
   Rejoice, good christian people,
   rejoice ye far and wide:
   In Mary see the stem;
   and who the flow'r but Jesus,
   the babe of Bethlehem?

2. This flower the prophet Esay
   foresaw and did foretell,
   born of the virgin mother;
   and man should love her well.
   Yet, stem, to flower give place,
   for from the same both angels
   and men derive solace.

3. He is the modest field-flower
   that in our vale is seen:
   or like the snow-white lily
   amid the briars keen.
   No rose so sweet and fair;
   no perfume aromatic
   can with his name compare.

4. This flower with fragrant odour
   doth woo the passer-by,
   and fill his very being
   with love right wondrously;
   sweet flower, for thee I sigh;
   thy grace my fainting spirit
   alone can satisfy.

Text: Translated from the Latin by George Ratcliffe Woodward (1848-1934)

36 A VIRGIN MOST PURE

1. A virgin most pure, as the prophets do tell, hath brought forth a baby, as it hath befell; to be our Redeemer from death, hell, and sin, which Adam's transgression had wrapped us in. Aye, and therefore be

2. In Bethlehem Jewry a city there was, where Joseph and Mary together did pass, and there to be taxéd with many one mo, for Caesar commanded the same should be so. Aye, and therefore be

3. But when they had entered the city so fair, a number of people so mighty was there, that Joseph and Mary, whose substance was small, could find in the inn there no lodging at all. Aye, and therefore be

mer - ry; re - joice, and be you mer - ry; set sor - row a -

side; Christ Je - sus our sa - viour was born at this tide.

4. Then they were constrain'd in a stable to lie,
   where horses and asses they used for to tie;
   their lodging so simple they took it no scorn,
   but a- / gainst the next / morning our / Saviour was / born.
   Refrain

5. The King of all kings to this world being brought,
   small store of fine linen to wrap him was sought;
   and when she had swaddled her young son so sweet,
   within an ox manger she laid him to sleep.
   Refrain

6. Then God sent an angel from heaven so high,
   to certain poor shepherds in fields where they lie,
   and bade them no longer in sorrow to stay,
   because that our Saviour was born on this day.
   Refrain

Text: Traditional
Music: From Gilbert's *Some Ancient Christmas Carols* (1822) arranged Charles Wood (1866-1926)

37 ANGELS FROM THE REALMS OF GLORY

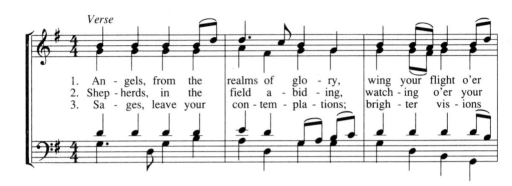

1. An - gels, from the realms of glo - ry, wing your flight o'er
2. Shep - herds, in the field a - bid - ing, watch - ing o'er your
3. Sa - ges, leave your con - tem - pla - tions; brigh - ter vis - ions

all the earth; ye who sang cre - a - tion's sto - ry
flocks by night, God with man is now re - sid - ing;
beam a - far; seek the great de - sire of na - tions:

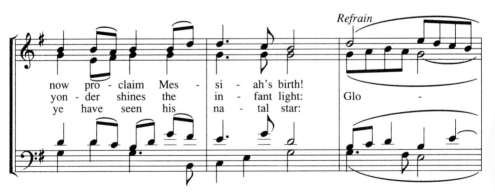

now pro - claim Mes - si - ah's birth! Glo -
yon - der shines the in - fant light:
ye have seen his na - tal star:

4. Saints, before the altar bending,
   watching long in hope and fear,
   suddenly the Lord, descending,
   in his temple shall appear:
       Refrain

5. Though an infant now we view him,
   he shall fill his Father's throne,
   gather all the nations to him;
   every knee shall then bow down:
       Refrain

Text: Traditional French translated by James Montgomery (1771-1854)
Music: French Melody arranged Richard Runciman Terry (1865-1938)

38 BLESSED BE THAT MAID MARY

Verse

1. Bles - sed be that maid Ma - ry; born he was of
2. In a man - ger of an ass Je - su lay and
3. Sweet and bliss - ful was the song chan - ted of the

her bo - dy: ve - ry God ere time be - gan.
lul - lèd was; born to die up - on the tree
an - gel throng, 'Peace on earth,' Al - le - lu - ya.

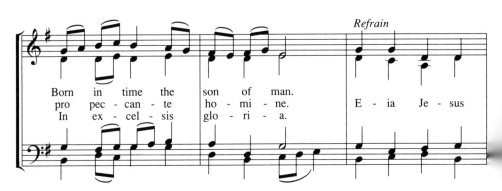

Born in time the son of man.
pro pec - can - te ho - mi - ne.
In ex - cel - sis glo - ri - a.

Refrain

E - ia Je - sus

ho - di - e   na - tus est de vir - gi - ne.

4. Fare three kings from far-off land,
   incense, gold and myrrh in hand;
   in Bethlem the babe they see,
   stelle ducti lumine.
   Refrain

5. Make we merry on this fest,
   In quo Christus natus est;
   on this child I pray you call
   to assoil and save us all.
   Refrain

Text: From the *Sloane* Manuscript (c.15th century)
Music: From William Ballet's Lute Book (c.1590) harmonised by Charles Wood (1866-1926)

39 COVENTRY CAROL (3-part)

Text: Robert Croo from the *Pageant of the Shearmen and Tailors* (1534)
Music: Original Tune of 1591

39a COVENTRY CAROL (4-part)

1. Lul - ly, lul - la, thou lit - tle ti-ny child,
2. O sis - ters too, how may we do,
3. He - rod the king, in his ra - ging,
4. That woe is me, poor child for thee!

by by, lul - ly lul - lay. Thou lit - tle ti-ny child, lul -
for to pre - serve this day this poor young - ling, for
char - gèd he hath this day his men of might, in
and e - ver morn and day, for thy part - ing nei-ther

ly lul - la; by by, lul - ly lul - lay.
whom we sing, by by lul - ly lul - lay?
his own sight, all young child - ren to slay.
say nor sing, by by, lul - ly lul - lay.

Text: Robert Croo from the *Pageant of the Shearmen and Tailors* (1534)
Music: Original Tune of 1591 arranged Neil Jenkins

40 DING DONG! MERRILY ON HIGH

Verse

1. Ding dong! mer-ri-ly on high in heav'n the bells are ring-ing:
2. E'en so here be-low, be-low, let stee-ple bells be swung-en,
3. Pray you, du-ti-ful-ly prime your mat-in chime, ye ring-ers;

Ding dong! ve-ri-ly the sky is riv'n with an-gel sing-ing.
and ee-o, ee-o, ee-o, by priest and peo-ple sung-en.
may you beau-ti-ful-ly rime your eve-time song, ye sing-ers.

Refrain

Glo-

ri-a, ho-san-na in ex-cel-sis!

Text: George Ratcliffe Woodward (1848-1934)
Music: Traditional French Melody arranged Charles Wood (1866-1926)

41 ECHO CAROL

Verse

1. While I my sheep did watch one night, lo, there ap-
2. Born is the child, in man - ger small, whom God hath
3. Go you this night, and you will find God's son so

Refrain

peared an an - gel bright.
sent to save us all. O sing with joy! sing with joy! sing with
pure, so sweet and kind.

joy! Christ is born! Christ is born! Christ is born! Be - ne - di - ca - mus Do - mi-

no! Be - ne - di - ca - mus Do - mi - no! Do - mi - no!

4. He has been sent from God above;
   he brings to man the gift of love.

5. If you will keep him in your heart,
   never will joy from you depart.

Text: Translated from the German by Ruth Heller
Music: German Melody arranged Neil Jenkins

42 HE IS BORN, THE HOLY ONE

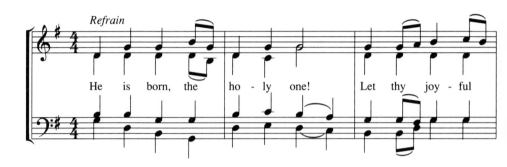

He is born, the ho - ly one! Let thy joy - ful

mu - sic ring! He is born, the ho - ly one!

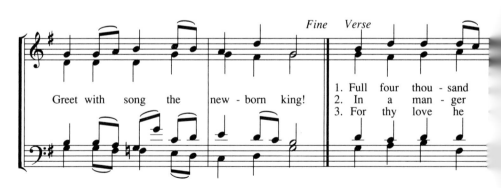

Greet with song the new - born king!

1. Full four thou - sand
2. In a man - ger
3. For thy love he

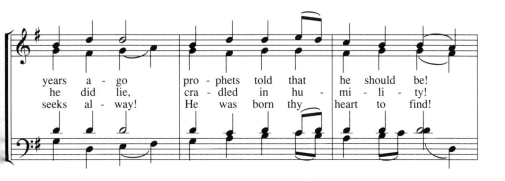

years a - go | pro - phets told that | he should be!
he did lie, | cra - dled in hu - | mi - li - ty!
seeks al - way! | He was born thy | heart to find!

Full four thou - sand | years a - go | sang they of his | ma - jes - ty!
In a man - ger | he did lie, | on a gen - tle | mai - den's knee.
For thy love he | seeks al - way! | Turn to him in | spi - rit kind!

No - el, No - el.

4. Greet him, princes of the east!
   Come, the infant to adore!
   Greet him, princes of the east!
   Loud your happy praises pour!
   Refrain

5. Herod sought him near and far!
   And his tender mother fled!
   Herod sought him near and far!
   But the babe was shelterèd.
   Refrain

Text: From *Dictionnaire de Noëls* translated by K.W. Simpson
Music: Melody taken from *Dictionnaire de Noëls* arranged Richard Runciman Terry (1865-1938)

43 I SAW THREE SHIPS

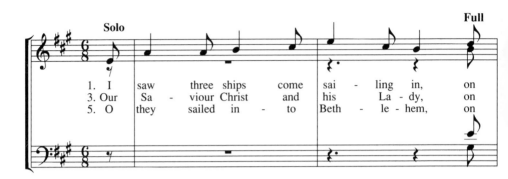

1. I saw three ships come sai - ling in, on
3. Our Sa - viour Christ and his La - dy, on
5. O they sailed in - to Beth - le - hem, on

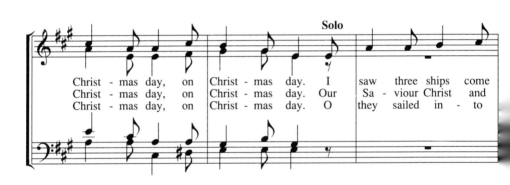

Christ - mas day, on Christ - mas day. I saw three ships come
Christ - mas day, on Christ - mas day. Our Sa - viour Christ and
Christ - mas day, on Christ - mas day. O they sailed in - to

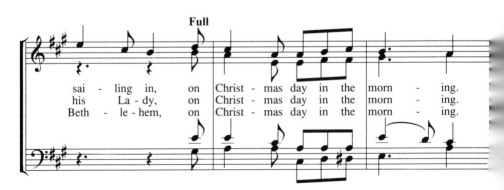

sai - ling in, on Christ - mas day in the morn - ing.
his La - dy, on Christ - mas day in the morn - ing.
Beth - le - hem, on Christ - mas day in the morn - ing.

2. And | what | was | in | those | ships | all | three, | on
4. Pray, | whi - | ther | sailed | those | ships | all | three, | on
6. And | all | the | bells | on | earth | shall | ring, | on

Christ - mas day | on | Christ - mas day? | And | what | was | in | those
Christ - mas day, | on | Christ - mas day? | Pray, | whi - | ther | sailed | those
Christ - mas day, | on | Christ - mas day. | And | all | the | bells | on

ships | all three, | on | Christ - mas day | in | the | morn - ing?
ships | all three, | on | Christ - mas day | in | the | morn - ing?
earth | shall ring, | on | Christ - mas day | in | the | morn - ing.

Performance Suggestion: The solo can be taken by either a male or female voice.

Text: Taken from William Sandys' *Christmas Carols, Ancient and Modern* (1833)
Music: Traditional English arranged Neil Jenkins

44 JOSEPH DEAREST, JOSEPH MINE

1. (Female) Jo - seph dear - est, Jo - seph mine, help me cra - dle the
2. (Male) Glad - ly, dear one, la - dy mine, help I cra - dle this

(Humming)

child di - vine; God re - ward thee and all that's thine in
child of thine; God's own light on us both shall shine in

to Refrain

pa - ra - dise, so prays the mo - ther Ma - ry.
pa - ra - dise, as prays the mo - ther Ma - ry.

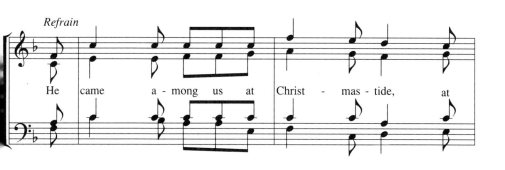

Refrain

He came a-mong us at Christ - mas-tide, at

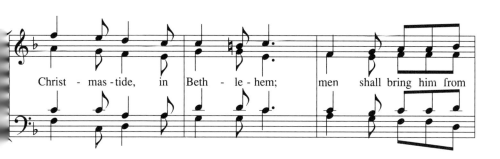

Christ - mas-tide, in Beth - le-hem; men shall bring him from

far and wide love's di - a-dem. Je - sus, Je - sus,

to Verses 2, 3, 4

lo, he comes and loves and saves and frees us!

Full

3. Peace to all that have good-will! God, who hea-ven and
4. All shall come and bow the knee; wise and hap-py their

earth doth fill, comes to turn us a-way from ill, and
souls shall be, lov-ing such a di-vi-ni-ty, as

to Refrain

lies so still with-in the crib of Ma - ry.
all may see in Je - sus, son of Ma - ry.

Text: Translated from the German by N.S.T.
Music: German (15th century) arranged George Ratcliffe Woodward (1848-1934) and Neil Jenkins

45 MARY'S BOY CHILD

Verse

1. Long time a-go in Beth - le - hem, so the Ho - ly Bi - ble say, Ma - ry's boy child, Je - sus Christ was born on Christ - mas day.

(Humming)

(Humming)

Ah

O hark, now!

Refrain

Hark, now hear the an - gels sing, a new king born to -

born

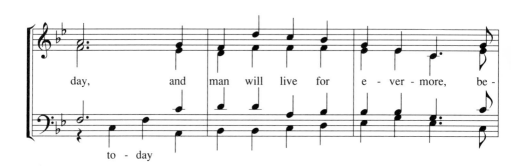

day, and man will live for e - ver - more, be -

to - day

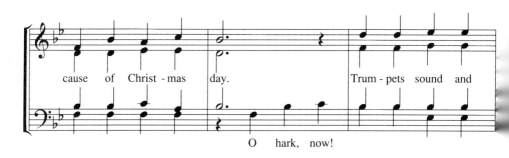

cause of Christ - mas day. Trum - pets sound and

O hark, now!

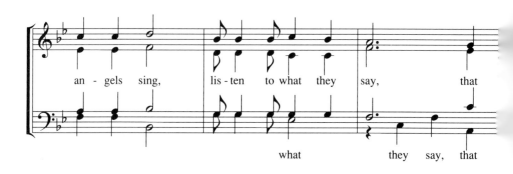

an - gels sing, lis - ten to what they say, that

what they say, that

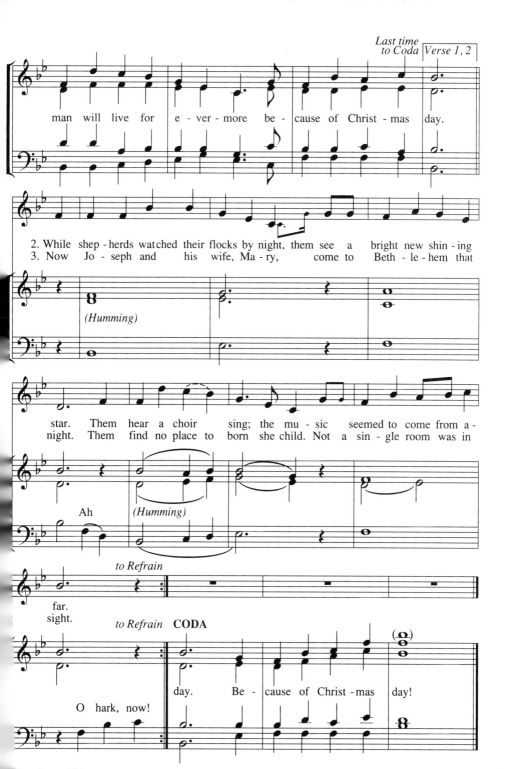

man will live for e - ver - more be - cause of Christ - mas day.

2. While shep - herds watched their flocks by night, them see a bright new shin - ing
3. Now Jo - seph and his wife, Ma - ry, come to Beth - le - hem that

(Humming)

star. Them hear a choir sing; the mu - sic seemed to come from a -
night. Them find no place to born she child. Not a sin - gle room was in

Ah *(Humming)*

to Refrain

far.
sight.

to Refrain **CODA**

day. Be - cause of Christ - mas day!

O hark, now!

Text: Jester Hairston
Music: Jester Hairston arranged Neil Jenkins

46 NOW THE HOLLY BEARS A BERRY

1. Now the hol - ly bears a ber - ry as
2. Now the hol - ly bears a ber - ry as
3. Now the hol - ly bears a ber - ry as
4. Now the hol - ly bears a ber - ry as

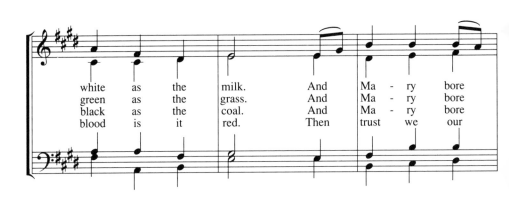

white as the milk. And Ma - ry bore
green as the grass. And Ma - ry bore
black as the coal. And Ma - ry bore
blood is it red. Then trust we our

Je - sus, who was wrapped up in silk:
Je - sus, who died on the cross.
Je - sus, who died for us all.
Sa - viour, who rose from the dead.

Text: From St Day, Cornwall, collected by Percy Dearmer (1867-1936)
Music: Traditional arranged Neil Jenkins

47 PAT-A-PAN

1. Wil - lie take your lit - tle drum, with your whis - tle,
2. Thus the men of old - en days loved the King of
3. God and man are now be - come more at one than

Ro - bin come! When we hear the fife and
kings to praise. When they hear the fife and
fife and drum. When you hear the fife and

drum, Tú - re - lú - re - lú, pá - ta - pá - ta - pán, when we
drum, Tú - re - lú - re - lú, pá - ta - pá - ta - pán, when they
drum, Tú - re - lú - re - lú, pá - ta - pá - ta - pán, when you

hear the fife and drum, Christ - mas should be fro - lic - some.
hear the fife and drum, sure our chil - dren won't be dumb!
hear the fife and drum, dance, and make the vil - lage hum!

Text: La Monnoye (1641-1728) translated by Percy Dearmer (1867-1936)
Music: Burgundian Melody arranged Charles Wood (1866-1926)

48 PERSONENT HODIE

1. Per - so - nent   ho - di - e   vo - ces pu - er - u - lae,
2. In mun - do   nas - ci - tur,   pan - nis in - vol - vi - tur,
3. Ma - gi tres   ve - ne - runt,   mu - ne - ra of - fe - runt,
4. Om - nes cle - ri - cu - li,   par - i - ter pu - e - ri,

lau - dan - tes   iu - cun - de   qui no - bis est
prae - se - pi   po - ni - tur   sta - bu - lo bru -
par - vu - lum   in - qui - runt,   stel - lu - lam se -
can - tent ut   an - ge - li: ad - ven - is - ti

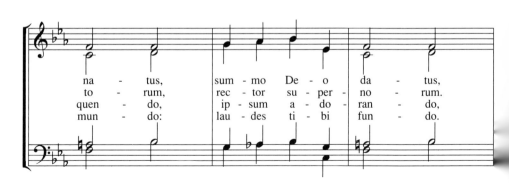

na - tus,   sum - mo De - o   da - tus,
to - rum,   rec - tor su - per - no - rum.
quen - do: ip - sum a - do - ran - do,
mun - do: lau - des ti - bi fun - do.

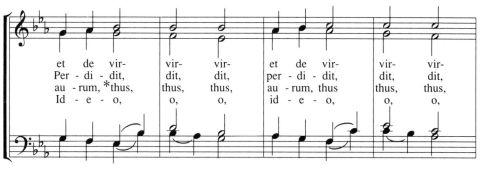

et	de	vir-	vir-	vir-	
Per -	di -	dit,	dit,	dit,	
au -	rum,	*thus,	thus,	thus,	
Id -	e -	o,	o,	o,	

et	de	vir-	vir-	vir-	
per -	di -	dit,	dit,	dit,	
au -	rum,	thus	thus,	thus,	
id -	e -	o,	o,	o,	

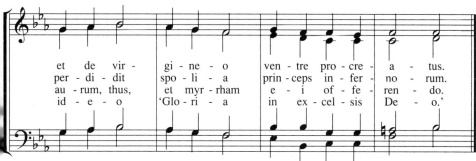

et	de	vir -	gi - ne - o	ven - tre	pro - cre -	a -	tus.
per -	di -	dit	spo - li - a	prin - ceps	in - fer -	no -	rum.
au -	rum,	thus,	et myr - rham	e - i	of - fe -	ren -	do.
id -	e -	o	'Glo - ri - a	in	ex - cel - sis	De -	o.'

* 'thus' pronounced as in 'benedic*tus*'.

Text: *Piae Cantiones* (1582)
Music: *Piae Cantiones* (1582) arranged Neil Jenkins

Alternative Text:

48a ON THIS DAY EARTH SHALL RING

1. On this day earth shall ring
   with the song children sing
   to the Son, Christ the King,
   born on earth to save us;
   Him the Father gave us.
   Ideo gloria in excelsis Deo!

2. His the doom, ours the mirth,
   when he came down to earth;
   Bethlehem saw his birth;
   ox and ass, beside him,
   from the cold would hide him.
   Ideo gloria in excelsis Deo!

3. God's bright star, o'er his head,
   wise men three to him led;
   kneel they low by his bed,
   lay their gifts before him,
   praise him and adore him.
   Ideo gloria in excelsis Deo!

4. On this day angels sing;
   with their song earth shall ring,
   praising Christ, heaven's King,
   born on earth to save us;
   peace and love he gave us.
   Ideo gloria in excelsis Deo!

Text: *Piae Cantiones* (1582) translated by Jane Joseph (1894-1929)

49 SEE AMID THE WINTER'S SNOW

Verse

1. See a-mid the win-ter's snow, born for us on earth be-low,
2. Lo, with-in a man-ger lies he who built the star-ry skies;
3. Say, ye ho-ly shep-herds, say, what your joy-ful news to-day;
5. Sa-cred in-fant, all di-vine, what a ten-der love was thine;

(Humming)

see, the ten-der lamb ap-pears, pro-mised from e-ter-nal years.
he, who throned in height sub-lime, sits a-mid the che-ru-bim!
where-fore have ye left your sheep on the lone-ly moun-tain steep?
thus to come from high-est bliss down to such a world as this!

Refrain

Hail! thou e-ver bless-ed morn! Hail, re-demp-tion's hap-py dawn!

Sing through all Je - ru - sa - lem, Christ is born in Beth - le - hem.

Full

4. 'As we watched at dead of night, lo, we saw a won - drous light;
6. Teach, O teach us, ho - ly child, by thy face so meek and mild,

to Refrain

an - gels sing - ing peace on earth, told us of the Sa - viour's birth.'
teach us to re - sem - ble thee, in thy sweet hu - mi - li - ty!

Text: Edward Caswall (1814-1878)
Music: John Goss (1800-1880) adapted Neil Jenkins

113

50 SHEPHERDS, IN THE FIELD ABIDING

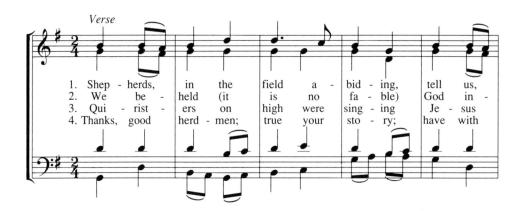

1. Shep - herds, in the field a - bid - ing, tell us,
2. We be - held (it is no fa - ble) God in -
3. Qui - rist - ers on high were sing - ing Je - sus
4. Thanks, good herd - men; true your sto - ry; have with

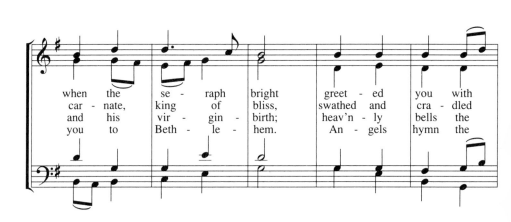

when the se - raph bright greet - ed you with
car - nate, king of bliss, swathed and cra - dled
and his vir - gin - birth; heav'n - ly bells the
you to Beth - le - hem. An - gels hymn the

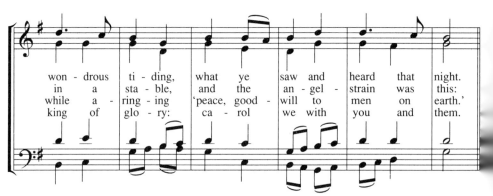

won - drous ti - ding, what ye saw and heard that night.
in a sta - ble, and the an - gel - strain was this:
while a - ring - ing 'peace, good - will to men on earth.'
king of glo - ry: ca - rol we with you and them.

Text: Translated from the Latin by George Ratcliffe Woodward (1848-1934)
Music: Traditional French Melody arranged Charles Wood (1866-1926)

51 SHEPHERDS! SHAKE OFF YOUR DROWSY SLEE

4. Cometh at length the age of peace;
   strife and sorrow now shall cease;
   prophets foretold the wondrous story
   of this heav'n-born Prince of Glory.

5. Shepherds! then up and quick away,
   seek the babe ere break of day;
   he is the hope of ev'ry nation,
   all in him shall find salvation.

Text and Music: Traditional French Carol arranged John Stainer (1840-1901)

52 SUSANI

1. From high - est heaven come, an - gels come! E -
2. And tune your mer - ry lay, ('tis meet) E -
3. Blend with your voi - ces, where ye sing E -
4. Sing peace on earth, from shore to shore, E -

ia! E - ia! Su - sa - ni, su - sa - ni, su - sa -

ni; with jo - cund song; with fife and drum.
ni; to harp and lute and vi - ol sweet. Al - le - lu -
ni; the or - gan and the trem - bling string.
ni; and praise your Lord for e - ver - more.

ia, Al - le - lu - ia. Of Je - sus sing and Ma - ri - a.

Text: From *Niederdeutsche Geistliche Lieder* (1524) translated by D.N.Y.
Music: German Carol Melody arranged Richard Runciman Terry (1863-1938)

53 THE ANGEL GABRIEL

1. The an - gel Ga - bri - el from hea - ven came, his
2. 'For known a bles - sed mo - ther thou shalt be; all

wings as drift - ed snow, his eyes as flame: 'All
ge - ne - ra - tions laud and ho - nour thee: Thy

hail', said he, 'thou low - ly maid - en Ma - ry. Most
son shall be Em - ma - nu - el, by seers fore - told Most

high - ly fa - voured la - dy!' Glo - ri - a!

3. Then gentle Mary meekly bowed her head;
   'to me be as it pleaseth God!' she said.
   'My soul shall laud and magnify his holy name.'
   Most highly favoured lady! Gloria!

4. Of her Emmanuel, the Christ, was born,
   in Bethlehem, all on a Christmas morn;
   and Christian folk throughout the world will ever say:
   Most highly favoured lady! Gloria!

Text: Sabine Baring-Gould (1834-1924)
Music: Traditional Basque Melody arranged Edgar Pettman (1865-1943)

54 THE FIRST NOWELL

Verse

1. The first no - well the an - gel did say was to
2. They look - èd up and saw a star, shin - ing
3. And by the light of that same star, three

cer - tain poor shep - herds in fields as they lay; in
in the east, be - yond them far, and
wise men came from coun - try far; to

fields where they lay keep - ing their sheep, on a
to the earth it gave their great light, and
seek for a king it was their in - tent, and to

Refrain

cold win - ter's night that was so deep.
so it con - tin - ued both day and night.
fol - low the star wher - e - ver it went.

No - well, no - well, no - well, no -

well, born is the King of Is - ra - el.

4. This star drew nigh to the north-west,
o'er Bethlehem it took its rest,
and there it did both stop and stay,
right over the place where Jesus lay.
Refrain

5. Then entered in those wise men three,
full rev'rently upon their knee,
and offered there, in his presence,
their gold, and myrrh, and frankincense.
Refrain

6. Then let us all with one accord,
sing praises to our heavenly Lord,
that hath made heaven and earth of naught,
and with his blood mankind hath bought.
Refrain

Text: Taken from William Sandys' *Christmas Carols, Ancient and Modern* (1833)
Music: Traditional English arranged John Stainer (1840-1901)

55 THE HOLLY AND THE IVY (1)

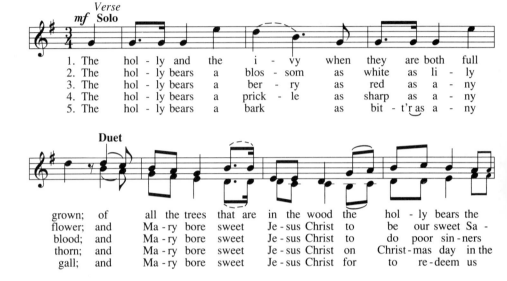

deer, the play - ing of the mer - ry or - gan, sweet

deer, the play - ing of the mer - ry or - gan, sweet

deer, the play - ing of the or - gan, sweet

deer, the play - ing of the or - gan sweet

4-part ending

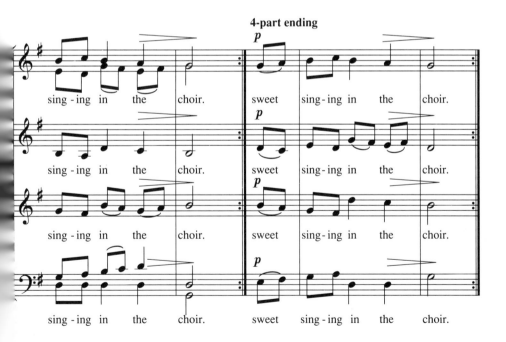

sing - ing in the choir. sweet sing - ing in the choir.

sing - ing in the choir. sweet sing - ing in the choir.

sing - ing in the choir. sweet sing - ing in the choir.

sing - ing in the choir. sweet sing - ing in the choir.

Text: Traditional English
Music: Traditional English Carol arranged Henry Walford Davies (1869-1941)

56 THE HOLLY AND THE IVY (2)

1. The hol - ly and the i - vy now both are full well
2. The hol - ly bears a blos - som as white as li - ly
3. The hol - ly bears a ber - ry as red as a - ny

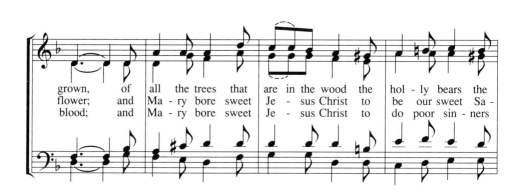

grown, of all the trees that are in the wood the hol - ly bears the
flower; and Ma - ry bore sweet Je - sus Christ to be our sweet Sa -
blood; and Ma - ry bore sweet Je - sus Christ to do poor sin - ners

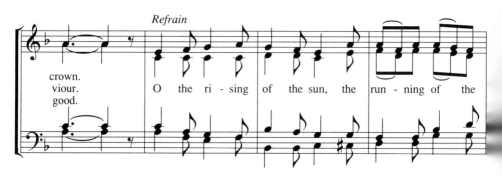

crown.
viour.   O the ri - sing of the sun, the run - ning of the
good.

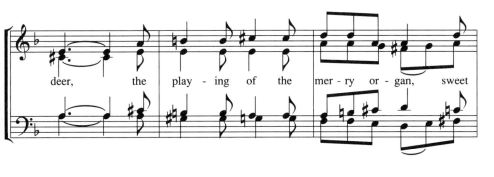

deer, the play - ing of the mer - ry or - gan, sweet

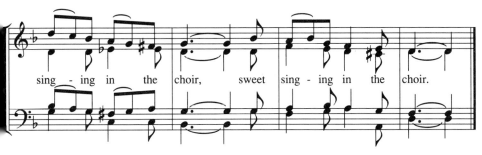

sing - ing in the choir, sweet sing - ing in the choir.

4. The holly bears a prickle,
as sharp as any thorn;
and Mary bore sweet Jesus Christ,
on Christmas Day in the morn.
Refrain

5. The holly bears a bark,
as bitter as any gall;
and Mary bore sweet Jesus Christ,
for to redeem us all.
Refrain

6. The holly and the ivy
now both are full well grown,
of all the trees that are in the wood,
the holly bears the crown.
Refrain

Text: Traditional English
Music: Old French Melody arranged John Stainer (1840-1901)

57 THE SEVEN JOYS OF MARY

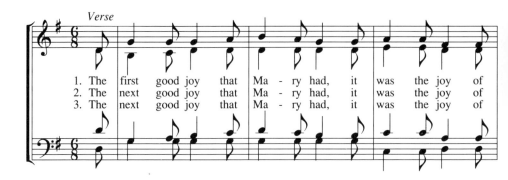

Verse

1. The first good joy that Ma - ry had, it was the joy of
2. The next good joy that Ma - ry had, it was the joy of
3. The next good joy that Ma - ry had, it was the joy of

one: to see her own son, Je - sus, when
two: to see her own son, Je - sus, to
three: to see her own son, Je - sus, to

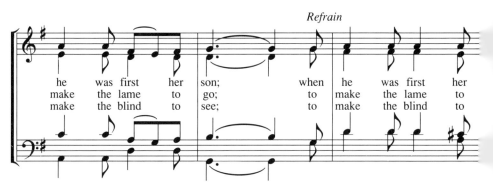

Refrain

he was first her son; when he was first her
make the lame to go; to make the lame to
make the blind to see; to make the blind to

son,
go, good man, and bless - ed may he be: sing
see,

Fa - ther, Son and Ho - ly Ghost, to all e - ter - ni - ty.

4. The next good joy that Mary had, it was the joy of four:
   to see her own son, Jesus, to read the Bible o'er;
   to read the Bible o'er, good man, and blessed may he be:
   sing Father, Son and Holy Ghost, to all eternity.

5. The next good joy that Mary had, it was the joy of five:
   to see her own son, Jesus, to make the dead alive;
   to make the dead alive, good man, and blessed may he be:
   sing Father, Son and Holy Ghost, to all eternity.

6. The next good joy that Mary had, it was the joy of six:
   to see her own son, Jesus, to bear the crucifix;
   to bear the crucifix, good man, and blessed may he be:
   sing Father, Son and Holy Ghost, to all eternity.

7. The next good joy that Mary had, it was the joy of seven:
   to see her own son, Jesus, to wear the crown of heaven;
   to wear the crown of heav'n, good man, and blessed may he be:
   sing Father, Son and Holy Ghost, to all eternity.

Text: Traditional English
Music: Traditional English Melody arranged Richard Runciman Terry (1865-1938)

58 THERE IS NO ROSE (2 or 3-part)

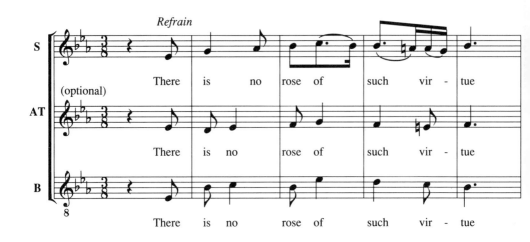

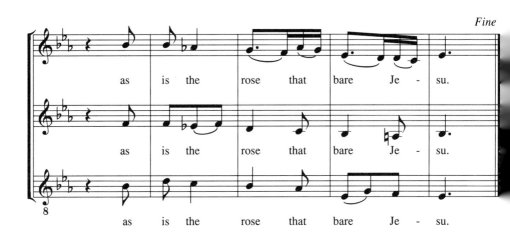

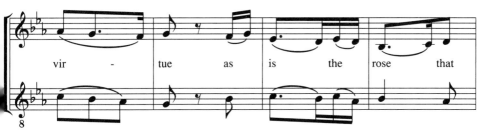

vir - tue as is the rose that

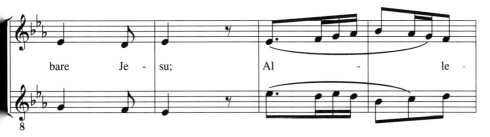

bare Je - su; Al - le -

D.C.

lu - - - ia.

2. For in this rose contained was
   heaven and earth in little space;
   Resmiranda.

3. By / that / rose we may well see
   that he is God in persons three;
   Pariforma.

4. The / angels / sung / en the / shepherds / to:
   Glo / ria / in ex / celsis De / o:
   Gaudeamus.

5. Leave / we / all this / world / ly / mirth,
   and follow we this joyful birth;
   Transeamus.

Text: Old English (15th century)
Music: From the *Trinity Roll* (c.1420)

59 UP! GOOD CHRISTEN FOLK

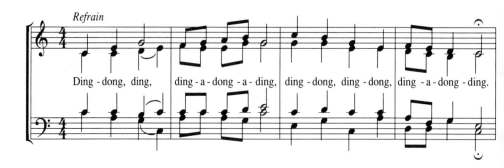

Ding - dong, ding, ding - a - dong - a - ding, ding - dong, ding - dong, ding - a - dong - ding.

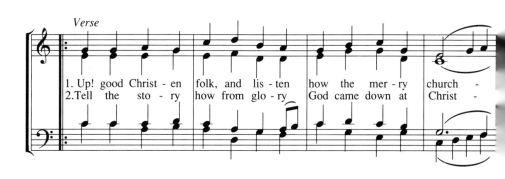

1. Up! good Christ - en folk, and lis - ten how the mer - ry church -
2. Tell the sto - ry how from glo - ry God came down at Christ -

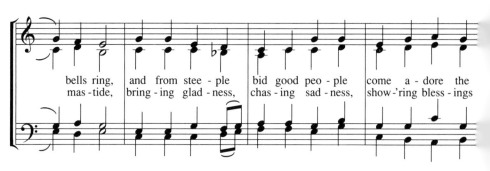

bells ring, and from stee - ple bid good peo - ple come a - dore the
mas - tide, bring - ing glad - ness, chas - ing sad - ness, show - 'ring bless - ings

new
far ——— born king: born of mo - ther,
and wide:

blest o'er o - ther, ex Ma - ri - a vir - gi - ne, in a sta - ble

('tis no fa - ble), Chris - tus na - tus ho - di - e.

Refrain

Ding - dong, ding, ding - a - dong - a - ding, ding - dong, ding - dong, ding - a - dong - ding.

Text: George Ratcliffe Woodward (1848-1934)
Music: From *Piae Cantiones* (1582) arranged George Ratcliffe Woodward (1848-1934)

60 WE THREE KINGS OF ORIENT ARE

Verse (3 soloists: humming in verses where no words are printed)

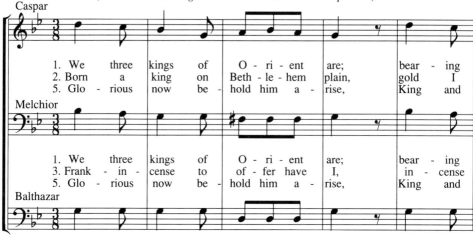

moor and moun - tain, fol - low - ing yon - der star.
ceas - ing ne - ver, o - ver us all to reign.
lu - ia'; 'Al - le - lu - ia' the earth re - plies.

moor and moun - tain, fol - low - ing yon - der star.
all men rais - ing, wor - ship him, God on high.
lu - ia'; 'Al - le - lu - ia' the earth re - plies.

moor and moun - tain, fol - low - ing yon - der star.
bleed - ing, dy - ing, sealed in the stone - cold tomb.
lu - ia'; 'Al - le - lu - ia' the earth re - plies.

Refrain

O star of won - der, star of night; star with

ro - yal beau - ty bright; west - ward lead - ing,

still pro - ceed - ing, guide us to thy per - fect light.

Text and Music: John Henry Hopkins (1820-1891)

61 WHEN THE CRIMSON SUN HAD SET

1. When the crim-son sun had set, low be-hind the win-try sea,
   on the bright and cold mid-night burst a sound of heav'n-ly glee:

Glo - - - ri-a in ex-cel-sis De - o, glo - ri-a in ex-cel-sis De - o.

2. Shepherds watching by their fold,
   on the crisp and hoary plain,
   in the sky bright hosts espy,
   singing in a gladsome strain,

3. Where the manger crib is laid,
   in the city fair and free,
   hand in hand this shepherd band,
   worship Christ on bended knee.

4. Join with us in welcome
   ye who in Christ's home
   sing the love of God abo
   shown at happy Christm

Text: G.P. Grantham
Music: Old French Carol arranged Samuel Stephenson Greatheed

Traditional Hymns & Carols

62 ADAM LAY Y-BOUNDEN (1)

Text: From the *Sloane* Manuscript (c.15th century)
Music: Boris Ord (1897-1961)

137

63 ADAM LAY Y-BOUNDEN (2)

With easy movement

A - dam lay y - boun - den, boun - den in a bond; four thou - sand win - ter thought he not too long. And all was for an ap - ple, an ap - ple that he took, as clerk - es find - en writ - ten in their book. Ne had the ap - ple tak - en been, the

Text: From the *Sloane* Manuscript (c.15th century)
Music: John Ireland (1879-1962)

64 ALL THIS NIGHT BRIGHT ANGELS SING

Moderato

1. All this night bright an - gels sing, ne - ver was such ca - rol - ling;
2. Wake, O earth, wake ev - ery - thing, wake and hear the joy I bring:

hark! a voice which loud - ly cries, 'mor - tals, mor - tals, wake and
wake and joy; for all this night, heav'n and ev - ery twink - ling

rise. Lo! to glad - ness turns your sad - ness:
light, all a - maz - ing, still stand gaz - ing;

from the earth is ris'n a sun, shines all night though day be done.'
an - gels, powers, and all that be, wake, and joy this sun to see.

© Copyright 1993 by Kevin Mayhew Ltd.
It is illegal to photocopy music.

140

Text: William Austin (c.1630)
Music: Arthur Sullivan (1842-1900)

65 AS JOSEPH WAS A-WALKING

As Joseph was a-walking he heard an angel sing: 'This night is born to Mary our heavenly King.' 1. He neither shall be born in housen nor in hall, nor

in the place of pa - ra - dise, but in an ox - en

stall. No - well! No - well!

2. He neither shall be clothèd
in / purple nor in / pall,
but / all in fair / linen
as / wear babies / all.
Nowell! Nowell!

3. He neither shall be rockèd
in / silver nor in / gold,
but / in a wooden / cradle
that / rocks on the / mould.
Nowell! Nowell!

4. He neither shall be christenèd
in / white wine nor in / red,
but / in the fair spring / water
as / we were christen / èd.
Nowell! Nowell!

Text: Traditional
Music: Richard Runciman Terry (1865-1938)

66 AS WITH GLADNESS MEN OF OLD

1. As with glad - ness men of old did the guid - ing star be - hold,
2. As with joy - ful steps they sped to that low - ly man - ger bed,
3. As they of - fered gifts most rare at that man - ger rude and bare,
4. Ho - ly Je - su, ev - 'ry day keep us in the nar - row way;
5. In the heav'n - ly coun - try bright need they no cre - a - ted light,

as with joy they hailed its light, lead - ing on - ward, beam - ing bright,
there to bend the knee be - fore him whom heav'n and earth a - dore,
so may we with ho - ly joy, pure, and free from sin's al - loy,
and, when earth - ly things are past, bring our ran - somed souls at last
thou its light, its joy, its crown, thou its sun which goes not down:

so, most gra - cious God may we e - ver - more be led to thee.
so may we with will - ing feet e - ver seek thy mer - cy - seat.
all our cost - liest trea - sures bring, Christ, to thee our heav'n - ly king.
where they need no star to guide, where no clouds thy glo - ry hide.
there for e - ver may we sing al - le - lu - ias to our king.

Text: William Chatterton Dix (1837-1898)
Music: Conrad Kocher (1786-1872) abridged by William Henry Monk (1823-1889)

67 CHERRY TREE CAROL

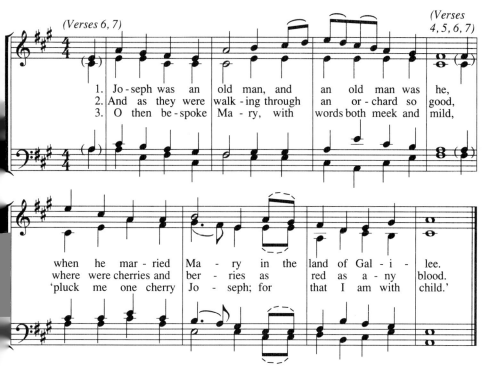

1. Jo-seph was an old man, and an old man was he,
2. And as they were walk-ing through an or-chard so good,
3. O then be-spoke Ma - ry, with words both meek and mild,

when he mar-ried Ma - ry in the land of Gal - i - lee.
where were cherries and ber - ries as red as a - ny blood.
'pluck me one cherry Jo - seph; for that I am with child.'

4. / 'Go to the tree, / Mary,
   and / it shall bow to / thee;
   and / you shall gather / cherries
   by / one, by two, by / three.'

5. / Then bowed down the / highest tree
   un / to his mother's / hand;
   'see,' / Mary cried, 'see, / Joseph,
   I have / cherries at com / mand.'

6. 'O / eat your cherries, / Mary,
   O / eat your cherries / now;
   O / eat your cherries, / Mary,
   that / grow upon the / bough.'

7. As / Joseph was a- / walking
   there / did an angel / sing;
   and / Mary's child at / midnight
   was / born to be our / king.

Text: Traditional English Ballad
Music: Traditional English arranged Martin Shaw (1875-1958)

68 CHRIST WAS BORN ON CHRISTMAS DAY (1

1. Christ was born on Christ-mas Day; wreath the hol - ly, twine the bay;
2. He is born to set us free; he is born our Lord to be,

Chris - tus na - tus ho - di - e, the babe, the son, the ho - ly one of
ex Ma - ri - a vir - gi - ne, the God, the Lord, by all a - dor'd for

Ma - ry. 3. Let the bright red ber - ries glow ev - 'ry - where in
e - ver. 4. Christ - ian men, re - joice and sing; 'tis the birth - day

good - ly show; Chris - tus na - tus ho - di - e, the babe, the son, the
of a King, ex Ma - ri - a vir - gi - ne, the God, the Lord, by

ho - ly one of Ma - ry.
all a - dor'd for e - ver. 5. Night of sad - ness,

morn of glad - ness e - ver-more; e - ver, e - ver.

Af - ter ma - ny trou - bles sore, morn of glad - ness

e - ver-more and e - ver - more. 6. Mid - night scarce - ly

pass'd and o - ver, draw - ing to this ho - ly morn;

Text: John Mason Neale (1818-1866)
Music: From *Piae Cantiones* (1582) arranged George Ratcliffe Woodward (1848-1934)

59 CHRIST WAS BORN ON CHRISTMAS DAY (2)

1. Christ was born on Christ-mas Day; wreathe the hol-ly, twine the bay. Chris-tus na-tus ho-di-e: The babe, the son, the ho-ly one of Ma-ry.
2. He is born to set us free; he is born our Lord to be, ex Ma-ri-a vir-gin-e: The babe, the son, the ho-ly one of Ma-ry.
3. Let the bright red ber-ries glow ev-'ry-where in good-ly show; Chris-tus na-tus ho-di-e: The babe, the son, the ho-ly one of Ma-ry.
4. Christ-ian men, re-joice and sing; 'tis the birth-day of a King, ex Ma-ri-a vir-gin-e: The God, the Lord, by all a-dored for e-ver.

Text: John Mason Neale (1818-1866)
Music: Richard Runciman Terry (1865-1938)

70 CHRISTIANS, AWAKE

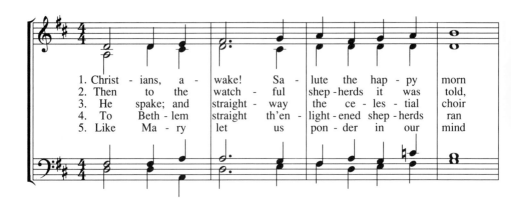

1. Christ - ians, a - wake! Sa - lute the hap - py morn
2. Then to the watch - ful shep - herds it was told,
3. He spake; and straight - way the ce - les - tial choir
4. To Beth - lem straight th'en - light - ened shep - herds ran
5. Like Ma - ry let us pon - der in our mind

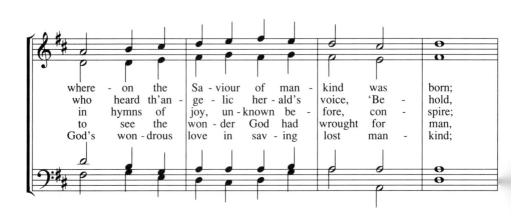

where - on the Sa - viour of man - kind was born;
who heard th'an - ge - lic her - ald's voice, 'Be - hold,
in hymns of joy, un - known be - fore, con - spire;
to see the won - der God had wrought for man,
God's won - drous love in sav - ing lost man - kind;

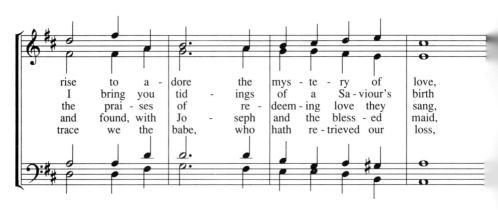

rise to a - dore the mys - te - ry of love,
I bring you tid - ings of a Sa - viour's birth
the prai - ses of re - deem - ing love they sang,
and found, with Jo - seph and the bless - ed maid,
trace we the babe, who hath re - trieved our loss,

which hosts of an - gels chant - ed from a - bove;
to you and all the na - tions on the earth:
and heaven's whole orb with al - le - lu - ias rang:
her son, the Sa - viour, in a man - ger laid:
from his poor man - ger to his bit - ter cross;

with them the joy - ful ti - dings first be - gun, of
this day hath God ful - filled his pro - mised word, this
God's high - est glo - ry was their an - them still, peace
then to their flocks, still prai - sing God, re - turn, and
then may we hope, an - ge - lic hosts a - mong, to

God in - car - nate and the vir - gin's son.
day is born a Sa - viour, Christ the Lord.'
on the earth, and un - to men good - will.
their glad hearts with ho - ly rap - ture burn.
sing, re - deemed, a glad tri - um - phal song.

Text: John Byrom (1692-1763)
Music: John Wainwright (1723-1768)

71 GOOD CHRISTIAN MEN, REJOICE

Text: John Mason Neale (1818-1866)
Music: Old German Melody arranged John Stainer (1840-1901)

72 GOOD KING WENCESLAS

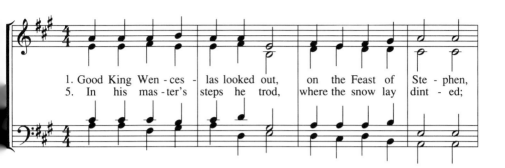

1. Good King Wen - ces - las looked out, on the Feast of Ste - phen,
5. In his mas - ter's steps he trod, where the snow lay dint - ed;

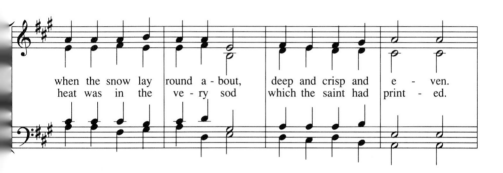

when the snow lay round a - bout, deep and crisp and e - ven.
heat was in the ve - ry sod which the saint had print - ed.

Bright - ly shone the moon that night, though the frost was cru - el,
There - fore, Chris - tian men, be sure, wealth or rank pos - ses - sing,

when a poor man | came in sight, | gath -'ring win - ter | fu - | el.
ye who now will | bless the poor, | shall your-selves find | bles - | sing.

℞ Solos

Male 2. | 'Hi - ther, page, and | stand by me, | if thou know'st it, | tel - ling,
Male 3. | 'Bring me flesh and | bring me wine, | bring me pine logs | hi - ther:
Treble 4. | 'Sire, the night is | dark - er now, | and the wind blows | strong - er;

(Humming)

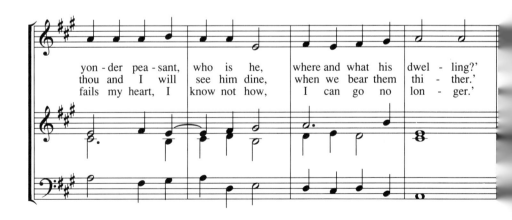

yon - der pea - sant, | who is he, | where and what his | dwel - ling?'
thou and I will | see him dine, | when we bear them | thi - ther.'
fails my heart, I | know not how, | I can go no | lon - ger.'

Text: John Mason Neale (1818-1866)
Music: From *Piae Cantiones* (1582) arranged John Stainer (1840-1901) and adapted Neil Jenkins

73 HAIL, BLESSED VIRGIN MARY

Text: George Ratcliffe Woodward (1848-1934)
Music: Italian Carol arranged Charles Wood (1866-1926)

74 HARK! THE HERALD ANGELS SING (1)

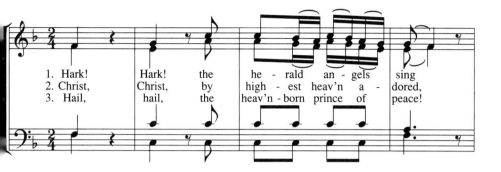

1. Hark! Hark! the he - rald an - gels sing
2. Christ, Christ, by high - est heav'n a - dored,
3. Hail, hail, the heav'n - born prince of peace!

glo - ry to the new - born king;
Christ, the e - ver - last - ing Lord;
Hail, the sun of right - eous - ness!

glo - ry to the
Christ, the e - ver -
Hail, the sun of

peace on earth and mer - cy mild,
late in time be - hold him come,
Light and life to all he brings,

peace on earth and mer - cy mild,
late in time be - hold him come,
Light and life to all he brings,

God   and   sin - ners   re - con - ciled!
off - spring   of   a   vir - gin's   womb.
risen   with   heal - ing   in   his   wings.

Joy - ful   all   ye   na - tions   rise,
Veiled   in   flesh   the   God - head   see;
Mild   he   lays   his   glo - ry   by,

join   the   tri - umph   (umph)   of   the   skies,
hail,   th' in - car - nate   (nate)   de - i - ty,
born   that   man   no   (no)   more   may   die,

with   th'an - ge - lic   host   pro - claim
pleased   as   man   with   man   to   dwell,
born   to   raise   the   sons   of   earth,

Text: C. Wesley (1707-1788), G. Whitefield (1714-1770), M. Madan (1726-1790) and others
Music: Attributed to Charles Burney (1726-1814) adapted by Neil Jenkins

75 HARK! THE HERALD ANGELS SING (2)

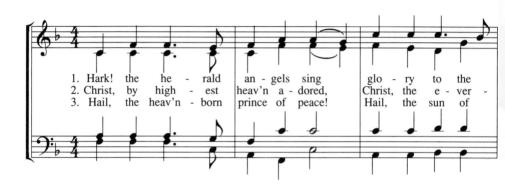

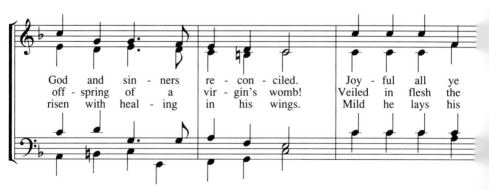

na - tions rise,   join   the   tri - umph
god - head see;   hail,   th'in - car - nate
glo - ry by,   born   that man   no

of   the skies,   with th'an - ge - lic   hosts pro - claim
de - i - ty!   Pleased as man with   man to   dwell,
more may die,   born to raise the   sons of   earth,

Christ is born in Beth - le - hem.   Hark! the her - ald
Je - sus, our Em - man - u - el.
born to give them se - cond birth.

an - gels sing   glo - ry   to   the   new - born king.

Text: C. Wesley (1707-1788), G. Whitefield (1714-1770), M. Madan (1726-1790) and others
Music: Felix Mendelssohn (1809-1847) from *Festgesang* (1844)

76 HOW FAR IS IT TO BETHLEHEM?

Text: Frances Chesterton (1869-1938)
Music: Traditional English Carol arranged Neil Jenkins

77 IN DULCI JUBILO (1)

1. In dul - ci ju - bi - lo, let
2. O Je - su, par - vu - le, I
3. O Pa - tris ca - ri - tas! O
4. U - bi sunt gau - dia where, if

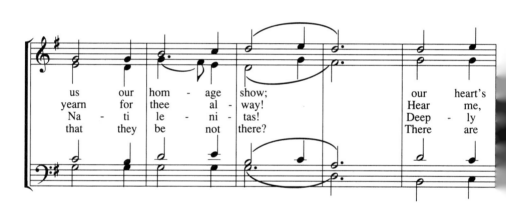

us our hom - age show; our heart's
yearn for thee al - way! Hear me,
Na - ti le - ni - tas! Deep - ly
that they be not there? There are

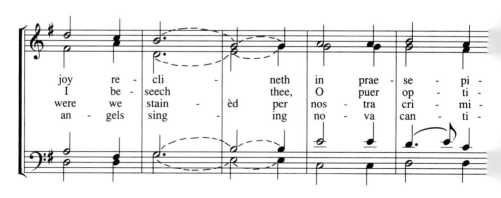

joy re - cli - neth in prae - se - pi -
I be - seech thee, O puer op - ti -
were we stain - èd per nos - tra cri - mi -
an - gels sing - ing no - va can - ti -

Text: Translated from the German by Robert Lucas Pearsall (1795-1856)
Music: Melody from *Geistliche Lieder* (1535) arranged Robert Lucas Pearsall (1795-1856)

77a IN DULCI JUBILO (2)

1. In dul - ci ju - bi - lo,   let

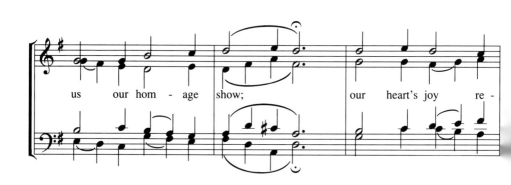

us   our hom - age show;   our   heart's joy   re -

cli - neth   in   prae - se - pi -
                 in   prae - se -

2. O Jesu, parvule,
   I yearn for thee alway!
   Hear me, I beseech thee,
   O puer optime!
   My prayer let it reach thee,
   O princeps gloriae!
   Trahe me post te!
   Trahe me post te!

3. O Patris caritas!
   O Nati lenitas!
   Deeply were we stainèd
   per nostra crimina;
   but thou has for us gainèd
   caelorum gaudia.
   O that we were there!
   O that we were there!

4. Ubi sunt gaudia, where,
   if that they be not there?
   There are angels singing
   nova cantica,
   and there the bells are ringing
   in regis curia.
   O that we were there!
   O that we were there!

Text: Translated from the German by Robert Lucas Pearsall (1795-1856)
Music: Melody from *Geistliche Lieder* (1535) arranged Johann Sebastian Bach (1685-1750)

78 IN THE BLEAK MIDWINTER

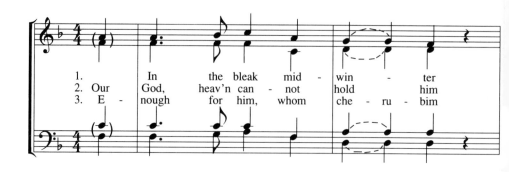

1.   In   the bleak   mid - win - ter
2. Our   God,   heav'n can - not   hold   him
3. E - nough   for him,   whom   che - ru - bim

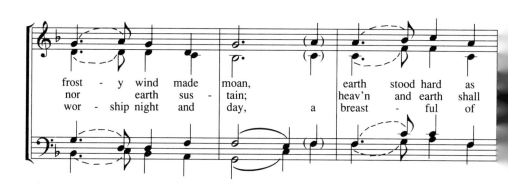

frost - y wind made   moan,   earth stood hard   as
nor   earth sus - tain;   a heav'n and earth   shall
wor - ship night and   day,   a breast - ful   of

i - ron,   wa - ter like   a   stone;
flee a - way   when he comes   to   reign:
milk   and a   man - ger - ful of   hay;   e -

snow had fal - len, | snow on snow, | snow on | snow, the
in the bleak mid - | win - ter a | sta - ble place suf - | ficed the
nough for him, whom | an - gels | fall down be - | fore, the

in the bleak mid - | win - ter, | long a - | go.
Lord God al - | might - y | Je - sus | Christ.
ox and ass and | ca - mel | which a - | dore.

4. / Angels and archangels may have gathered there,
/ cherubim and seraphim thronged the air:
but / only his mother in her maiden bliss
/ worshipped the beloved with a kiss.

5. / What can I give him, poor as I am?
/ If I were a shepherd I would bring a lamb;
/ if I were a wise man I would do my part;
yet / what I can I give him: give my heart.

Text: Christina Rossetti (1830-1894)
Music: Gustav Holst (1874-1934)

79 IT CAME UPON THE MIDNIGHT CLEAR

1. It came up - on the mid - night clear, that
2. Still through the clo - ven skies they come, with

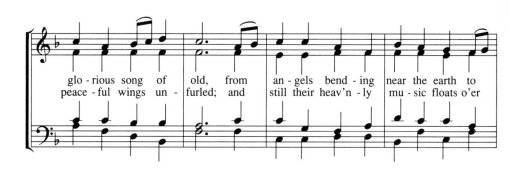

glo - rious song of old, from an - gels bend - ing near the earth to
peace - ful wings un - furled; and still their heav'n - ly mu - sic floats o'er

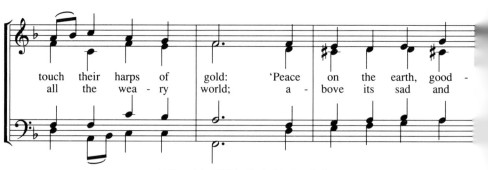

touch their harps of gold: 'Peace on the earth, good -
all the wea - ry world; a - bove its sad and

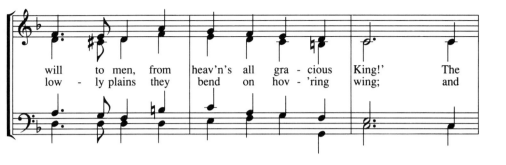

will   to men, from   heav'n's all   gra - cious   King!'   The
low - ly plains they   bend   on   hov - 'ring   wing;   and

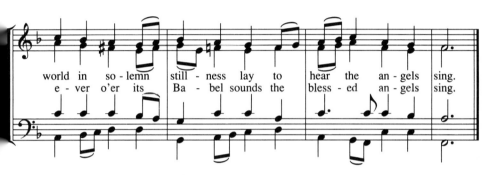

world in   so - lemn   still - ness lay   to   hear   the   an - gels   sing.
e - ver o'er   its   Ba - bel sounds the   bless - ed   an - gels   sing.

3. Yet with the woes of sin and strife
the world has suffered long;
beneath the angel strain have rolled
two thousand years of wrong;
and man, at war with man, hears not
the love-song which they bring:
O hush the noise, ye men of strife,
and hear the angels sing!

4. For lo! the days are hastening on
by prophet bards foretold,
when, with the ever-circling years,
comes round the age of gold;
when peace shall over all the earth
its ancient splendours fling,
and the whole world give back the song
which now the angels sing.

Text: Edmund Hamilton Sears (1810-1876)
Music: Traditional English Melody arranged Arthur Sullivan (1842-1900)

80 LEAVE, SHEPHERDS, LEAVE

Allegro vivace

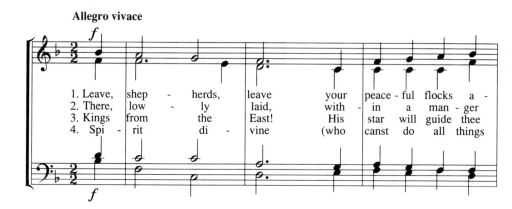

1. Leave, shep - herds, leave your peace - ful flocks a -
2. There, low - ly laid, with - in a man - ger
3. Kings from the East! His star will guide thee
4. Spi - rit di - vine (who canst do all things

graz - ing! No long - er grieve but
nar - row, a love - ly maid and
tru - ly! Where he doth rest in
sure - ly), our hearts en - shrine thine

come, O come a - way! Come and a -
in - fant thou shalt see! His ten - der
love and faith draw near: our ris - ing
ar - dours sweet and fair! For peace is

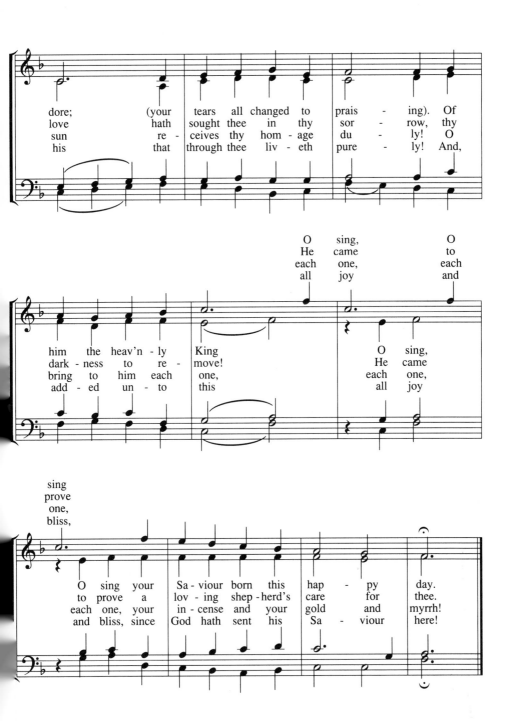

Text: French Noël translated by K.W. Simpson
Music: Traditional French Melody arranged Richard Runciman Terry (1865-1938)

81 LITTLE DONKEY

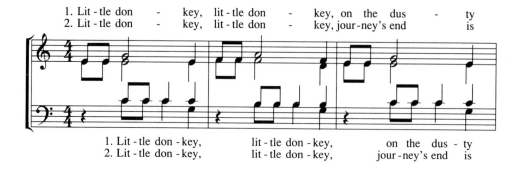

1. Lit-tle don - key, lit-tle don - key, on the dus - ty
2. Lit-tle don - key, lit-tle don - key, jour-ney's end is

1. Lit - tle don - key, lit - tle don - key, on the dus - ty
2. Lit - tle don - key, lit - tle don - key, jour - ney's end is

road. Got to keep on plod-ding on - wards
near. There are wise men wait-ing for a

dus - ty road. Plod - ding on - wards
is near. Wait - ing for a

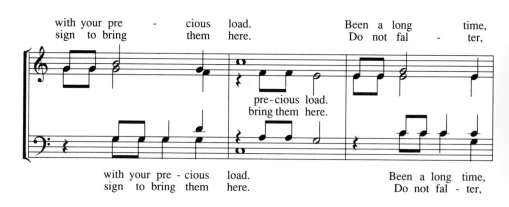

with your pre - cious load. Been a long time,
sign to bring them here. Do not fal - ter,

with your pre - cious load. Been a long time,
sign to bring them here. Do not fal - ter,

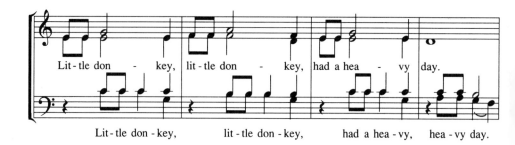

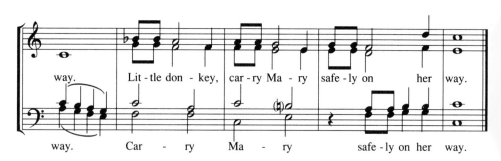

Text and Music: Eric Boswell arranged Neil Jenkins

82 O COME, ALL YE FAITHFUL (1)

1. O come, all ye faith - ful, joy - ful and tri - um - phant, O
2. God of God, light of light,
3. See how the shep - herds sum - moned to his cra - dle,
4. Lo, star - led chief - tains, Ma - gi, Christ a - dor - ing,
5. Child, for us sin - ners poor and in the man - ger,

come ye, O come ye to Beth - le - hem!
lo! he ab - hors not the vir - gin's womb;
lea - ving their flocks, draw nigh with low - ly fear;
of - fer him in - cense, gold and myrrh;
fain we em - brace thee with awe and love;

Come and be - hold him, born the King of an - gels!
ve - ry God, be - got - ten, not cre - a - ted:
we, too, will thi - ther bend our joy - ful foot - steps: O
we to the Christ - child bring our heart's ob - la - tions.
who would not love thee, lov - ing us so dear - ly?

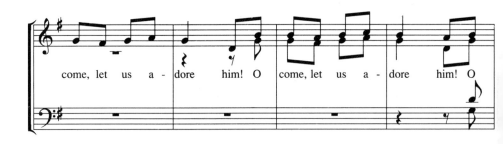

come, let us a - dore him! O come, let us a - dore him! O

come let us a - dore him, Christ the Lord!

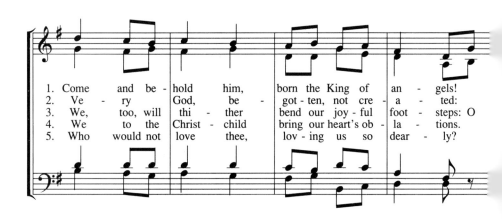

1. Come and be - hold him, born the King of an - gels!
2. Ve - ry God, be - got - ten, not cre - a - ted:
3. We, too, will thi - ther bend our joy - ful foot - steps: O
4. We to the Christ - child bring our heart's ob - la - tions.
5. Who would not love thee, lov - ing us so dear - ly?

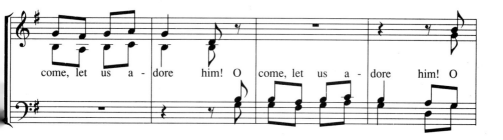

come, let us a - dore him! O come, let us a - dore him! O

come let us a - dore him, Christ the Lord!

6. / Sing, choirs of / angels!
/ Sing in exul / tation!
/ Sing, all ye citizens of / heaven a / bove:
/ 'Glory to / God
/ in the / highest.'
O come, let us adore him!
O come, let us adore him!
O come let us adore him,
Christ the Lord! (*repeat*)

7. / Yea, Lord, we / greet thee,
/ born this happy / morning,
/ Jesu, to / thee be / glory / given;
/ word of the / Father,
/ now in flesh ap / pearing:
O come, let us adore him!
O come, let us adore him!
O come let us adore him,
Christ the Lord! (*repeat*)

Text: Translated from the Latin by F. Oakeley (1802-1880), W.T. Brooke (1848-1917) and others
Music: John Francis Wade (1711-1786) arranged Thomas Greatorex (1757-1831)

82a O COME, ALL YE FAITHFUL (2)

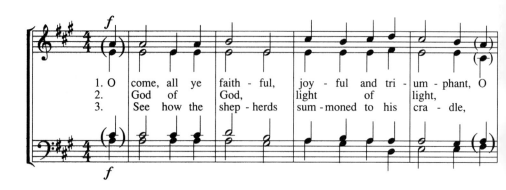

1. O come, all ye faith - ful, joy - ful and tri - um - phant, O
2. God of God, light of light,
3. See how the shep - herds sum - moned to his cra - dle,

come ye, O come ye to Beth - le - hem!
lo! he ab - hors not the vir - gin's womb;
leav - ing their flocks, draw nigh with low - ly fear;

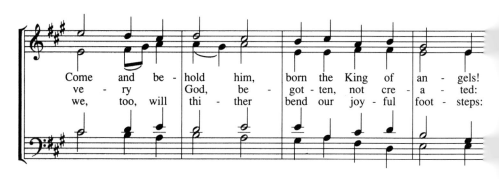

Come and be - hold him, born the King of an - gels!
ve - ry God, be - got - ten, not cre - a - ted:
we, too, will thi - ther bend our joy - ful foot - steps:

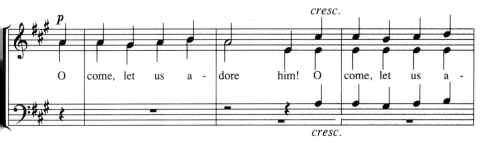

4. / Lo, star-led / chieftains,
/ Magi, Christ a / doring,
/ offer him / incense, / gold and myrrh;
/ we to the / Christ-child
/ bring our heart's ob / lations.
O come let us adore him, Christ the Lord!

5. / Child, for us / sinners
/ poor and in the / manger,
/ fain we em / brace thee with / awe and love;
/ who would not / love thee,
/ loving us so / dearly?
O come let us adore him, Christ the Lord!

6. / Sing, choirs of / angels!
/ Sing in exul / tation!
/ Sing, all ye citizens of / heaven a / bove:
/ 'Glory to / God
/ in the / highest.'
O come let us adore him, Christ the Lord!

7. / Yea, Lord, we / greet thee,
/ born this happy / morning,
/ Jesu, to / thee be / glory / given;
/ word of the / Father,
/ now in flesh ap / pearing:
O come let us adore him, Christ the Lord!

Text: Translated from the Latin by F. Oakeley (1802-1880), W.T. Brooke (1848-1917) and others
Music: John Francis Wade (1711-1786)

83 O LITTLE TOWN OF BETHLEHEM (1)

1. O lit - tle town of Beth - le - hem, how
2. O morn - ing stars, to - ge - ther pro -
3. How si - lent - ly, how si - lent - ly, the
4. O ho - ly child of Beth - le - hem, des -

still we see thee lie! A - bove thy deep and
claim the ho - ly birth, and prai - ses sing to
won - drous gift is giv'n! So God im - parts to
cend to us, we pray; cast out our sin, and

dream - less sleep the si - lent stars go by. Yet
God the King, and peace to men on earth; for
hu - man hearts the bless - ings of his heaven. No
en - ter in, be born in us to - day. We

in thy dark streets shin - eth the e - ver - last - ing
Christ is born of Ma - ry; and, gath - ered all a -
ear may hear his com - ing; but in this world of
hear the Christ - mas an - gels the great glad tid - ings

light; the hopes and fears of all the years are
bove, while mor - tals sleep, the an - gels keep their
sin, where meek souls will re - ceive him, still the
tell: O come to us, a - bide with us, our

met in thee to - night.
watch of wond - 'ring love.
dear Christ en - ters in.
Lord Em - man - u - el.

Text: Phillips Brooks (1835-1893)
Music: Henry Walford Davies (1869-1941)

84 O LITTLE TOWN OF BETHLEHEM (2)

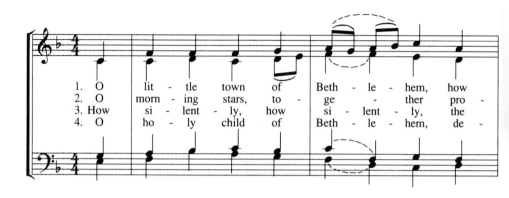

1. O lit - tle town of Beth - le - hem, how
2. O morn - ing stars, to - ge - ther pro -
3. How si - lent - ly, how si - lent - ly, the
4. O ho - ly child of Beth - le - hem, de -

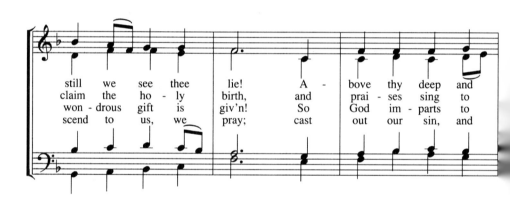

still we see thee lie! A - bove thy deep and
claim the ho - ly birth, and prai - ses sing to
won - drous gift is giv'n! So God im - parts to
scend to us, we pray; cast out our sin, and

dream - less sleep the si - lent stars go by. Yet
God the King, and peace to men on earth; for
hu - man hearts the bless - ings of his heaven. No
en - ter in, be born in us to - day. We

in   thy dark streets shin - eth the
Christ is born of Ma - ry; and,
ear may hear his com - ing; but
hear the Christ - mas an - gels the

e - ver - last - ing light; the hopes and fears of
gath - ered all a - bove, while mor - tals sleep, the
in this world of sin, where meek souls will re -
great glad tid - ings tell: O come to us, a -

all the years are met in thee to - night.
an - gels keep their watch of wond - 'ring love.
ceive him, still the dear Christ en - ters in.
bide with us, our Lord Em - man - u - el.

Text: Phillips Brooks (1835-1893)
Music: Traditional English Melody collected and harmonized by Ralph Vaughan Williams (1872-1958)

85 O LITTLE TOWN OF BETHLEHEM (3)

Not too fast

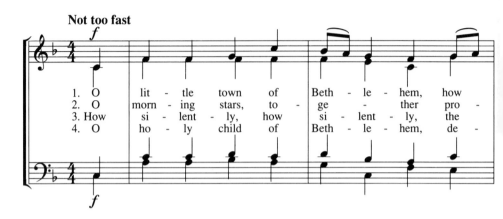

1. O lit - tle town of Beth - le - hem, how
2. O morn - ing stars, to - ge - ther pro -
3. How si - lent - ly, how si - lent - ly, the
4. O ho - ly child of Beth - le - hem, de -

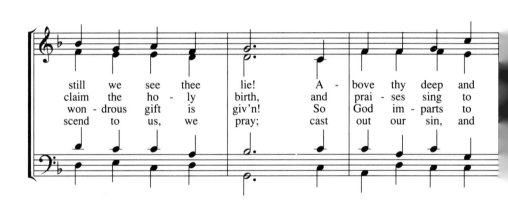

still we see thee lie! A - bove thy deep and
claim the ho - ly birth, and prai - ses sing to
won - drous gift is giv'n! So God im - parts to
scend to us, we pray; cast out our sin, and

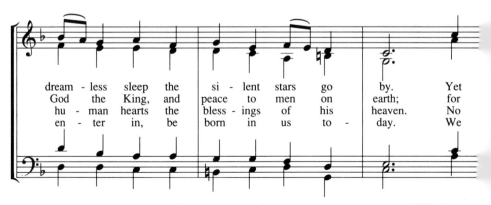

dream - less sleep the si - lent stars go by. Yet
God the King, and peace to men on earth; for
hu - man hearts the bless - ings of his heaven. No
en - ter in, be born in us to - day. We

in thy dark streets shin - eth the e - ver - last - ing
Christ is born of Ma - ry; and, gath - ered all a -
ear may hear his com - ing; but in this world of
hear the Christ - mas an - gels the great glad tid - ings

light; the hopes and fears of all the years
bove, while mor - tals sleep, the an - gels keep
sin, where meek souls will re - ceive him, still
tell: O come to us, a - bide with us,

are met in thee to - night.
their watch of wond - 'ring love.
the dear Christ en - ters in.
our Lord Em - man - u - el.

Text: Phillips Brooks (1835-1893)
Music: Melody collected by Sabine Baring-Gould (1834-1924) arranged Edgar Pettman (1865-1943)

86 ONCE IN ROYAL DAVID'S CITY (1)

1. Once in roy - al Da - vid's ci - ty stood a
2. He came down to earth from hea - ven who is
3. And through all his won - drous child - hood he would

low - ly cat - tle shed, where a mo - ther laid her
God and Lord of all, and his shel - ter was a
hon - our and o - bey, love, and watch the low - ly

ba - by in a man - ger for his
sta - ble, and his cra - dle was a
mai - den, in whose gen - tle arms he

bed.   Ma - ry   was   that mo - ther   mild,   Je - sus
stall.   With the   poor   and mean and   low-ly,   lived on
lay;   Christ - ian   chil - dren all must   be   mild,   o -

Christ   her lit - tle   child.
earth   our Sa - viour   ho - ly.
be - dient, good as   he.

4. For he is our childhood's pattern,
day by day like us he grew;
he was little, weak and helpless,
tears and smiles like us he knew;
and he feeleth for our sadness,
and he shareth in our gladness.

5. And our eyes at last shall see him
through his own redeeming love;
for that child so dear and gentle
is our Lord in heaven above;
and he leads his children on
to the place where he is gone.

6. Not in that poor lowly stable,
with the oxen standing by,
we shall see him; but in heaven,
set at God's right hand on high;
where, like stars, his children crowned,
all in white shall wait around.

Text: Cecil Frances Alexander (1823-1895)
Music: Henry John Gauntlett (1805-1876)

86a ONCE IN ROYAL DAVID'S CITY (2)

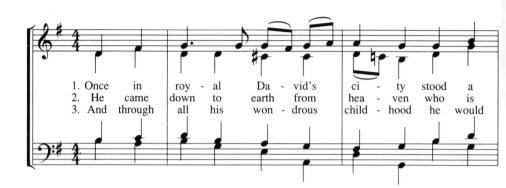

1. Once in roy - al Da - vid's ci - ty stood a
2. He came down to earth from hea - ven who is
3. And through all his won - drous child - hood he would

low - ly cat - tle shed, where a mo - ther laid her
God and Lord of all, and his shel - ter was a
ho - nour and o - bey, love, and watch the low - ly

ba - by in a man - ger for his
sta - ble, and his cra - dle was a
mai - den, in whose gen - tle arms he

bed.   Ma - ry   was   that   mo - ther mild,   Je - sus
stall.   With the   poor   and mean and low - ly,   lived on
lay;   Christ - ian chil - dren all must be   mild,   o -

Christ   her lit - tle   child.
earth   our Sa - viour ho - ly.
be - dient, good as he.

4. For he is our childhood's pattern,
day by day like us he grew;
he was little, weak and helpless,
tears and smiles like us he knew;
and he feeleth for our sadness,
and he shareth in our gladness.

5. And our eyes at last shall see him
through his own redeeming love;
for that child so dear and gentle
is our Lord in heaven above;
and he leads his children on
to the place where he is gone.

6. Not in that poor lowly stable,
with the oxen standing by,
we shall see him; but in heaven,
set at God's right hand on high;
where, like stars, his children crowned,
all in white shall wait around.

Text: Cecil Frances Alexander (1823-1895)
Music: Henry John Gauntlett (1805-1876) harmonized by Arthur Henry Mann (1850-1929)

87 REJOICE AND BE MERRY

1. Re - joice and be mer - ry in songs and in mirth! O praise our Re - deem - er, all mor - tals on earth! For this is the birth - day of Je - sus our King, who brought us sal - va - tion: his prais - es we'll sing!

2. A hea - ven - ly vi - sion ap - peared in the sky! Vast num - bers of an - gels the shep - herds did spy, pro - claim - ing the birth - day of Je - sus our King.

3. Like - wise a bright star in the sky did ap - pear, which led the wise men from the east to draw near; they found the Mes - si - ah, sweet Je - sus our King.

4. And when they were come, they their trea - sures un - fold, and un - to him off - ered myrrh, in - cense, and gold. So bless - èd for e - ver be Je - sus our King.

Text: Old English
Music: Old English arranged Richard Runciman Terry (1865-1938)

88 REMEMBER, O THOU MAN

1. Re - mem - ber, O thou man, O thou man, O thou man,

re - mem - ber, O thou man, thy time is spent.

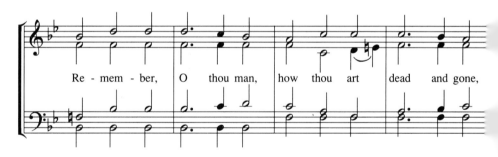

Re - mem - ber, O thou man, how thou art dead and gone,

and I did what I can, there - fore re - pent.

2. The angels all did sing,
   O thou man, O thou man,
   the angels all did sing,
   upon the hill.
   The angels all did sing
   praise to our heavenly King,
   and peace to man living,
   with a good will.

3. To Bethlem did they go,
   O thou man, O thou man,
   to Bethlem did they go,
   the shepherds three.
   To Bethlem did they go,
   to see where it were so,
   if Christ were born or no
   to set men free.

4. In Bethlem he was born,
   O thou man, O thou man,
   in Bethlem he was born,
   for mankind's sake.
   In Bethlem he was born
   for us that were forlorn,
   and therefore took no scorn,
   our flesh to take.

5. Give thanks to God alway,
   O thou man, O thou man,
   give thanks to God alway,
   most joyfully.
   Give thanks to God alway
   for this our happy day;
   let all men sing and say:
   Holy, holy.

ext: From *Melismata* (1611)
Music: Melody taken frrom *Melismata* (1611) arranged Thomas Ravenscroft (c.1590-c.1633)

89 SUSSEX CAROL

Text: Traditional English
Music: Traditional English Melody arranged Neil Jenkins

90 UNTO US IS BORN A SON

1. Un - to us is born a son, King of choirs su -
   per - nal; see on earth his life be - gun, of
   lords the Lord e - ter - nal, of lords the Lord e - ter - nal.

2. Christ from heav'n de - scend - ing low, comes on earth a
   stran - ger; ox and ass their own - er know, be -
   cra - dled in the man - ger, be - cra - dled in the man - ger.

3. This did He - rod sore af - fray, and grie - vous - ly be -
   wil - der, so he gave the word to slay, and
   slew the lit - tle chil - der, and slew the lit - tle chil - der.

4. Of his love and mercy mild
   this the Christmas story,
   and / O that Mary's gentle child
   might lead us up to glory,
   might lead us up to glory!

5. O and A, and A and O,
   cum / cantibus in choro;
   let our merry organ go,
   Benedicamus / Domi / no,
   Benedicamus / Domi / no.

Text: Translated from the Latin by George Ratcliffe Woodward (1848-1934)
Music: From *Piae Cantiones* (1582) arranged Neil Jenkins

91 WHAT CHILD IS THIS?

1. What child is this, who, laid to rest, on Ma - ry's lap is
2. Why lies he in such mean es - tate, where ox and ass are
3. So bring him in - cense, gold and myrrh, come pea - sant, king, to

sleep - ing? Whom an - gels greet with an - thems sweet, while
feed - ing? Good Christ - ian, fear: for sin - ners here the
own him: the King of kings sal - va - tion brings, let

shep - herds watch are keep - ing? This, this is
si - lent Word is plead - ing: Nails, spear, shall
lov - ing hearts en - throne him. Raise, raise the

Christ the king, whom shep - herds guard and an - gels sing:
pierce him through, the cross be borne for me, for you:
song on high, the vir - gin sings her lull - a - by:

haste, haste to bring him laud, the babe, the son of Ma - ry!
hail, hail, the Word made flesh, the babe, the son of Ma - ry!
joy, joy, for Christ is born, the babe, the son of Ma - ry!

Text: William Chatterton Dix (1837-1898)
Music: Traditional English Melody arranged John Stainer (1840-1901)

92 WHENCE IS THAT GOODLY FRAGRANCE

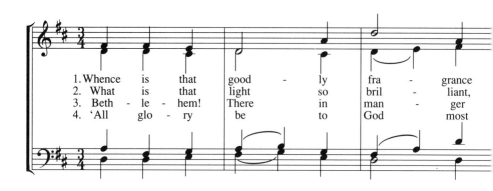

1. Whence is that good - ly fra - grance
2. What is that light so bril - liant,
3. Beth - le - hem! There in man - ger
4. 'All glo - ry be to God most

flow - ing, steal - ing our sen - ses all a -
break - ing here in the night a - cross our
ly - ing, find your Re - deem - er, haste a -
ho - ly, and on the earth let there be

way? Ne - ver the like did come a -
eyes? Ne - ver so bright, the day - star
way; run ye with ea - ger foot - steps
peace.' Thus an - gels sang to shep - herds

blow - ing, shep - herds, in flow - 'ry
wak - ing, start - ed to climb the
hie - ing! Wor - ship the Sa - viour
low - ly: 'Good - will be - gin and

fields in May. Whence is that
morn - ing skies! What is that
born to - day. Beth - le - hem!
ne - ver cease.' 'All glo - ry

good - ly fra - grance flow - ing,
light so bril - liant, break - ing
There in man - ger ly - ing,
be to God most ho - ly,

steal - ing our sen - ses all a - way?
here in the night a - cross our eyes?
find your Re - deem - er, haste a - way.
and on the earth let there be peace.'

Text: Translated from the French by Allen Beville Ramsay (1872-1955) and Neil Jenkins
Music: French Noël arranged Richard Runciman Terry (1865-1938)
201

92a WHENCE IS THAT GOODLY FRAGRANCE (2

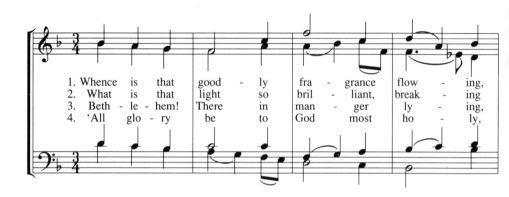

1. Whence is that good - ly fra - grance flow - ing,
2. What is that light so bril - liant, break - ing
3. Beth - le - hem! There in man - ger ly - ing,
4. 'All glo - ry be to God most ho - ly,

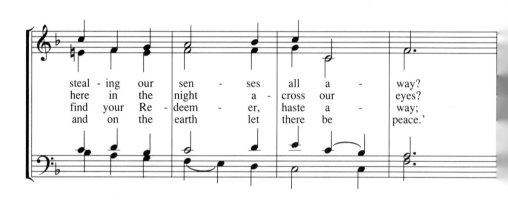

steal - ing our sen - ses all a - way?
here in the night a - cross our eyes?
find your Re - deem - er, haste a - way;
and on the earth let there be peace.'

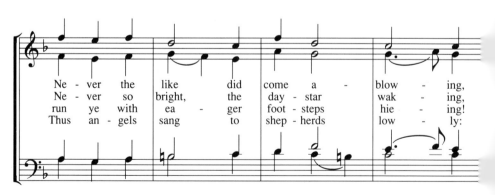

Ne - ver the like did come a - blow - ing,
Ne - ver so bright, did the day - star wak - ing,
run ye with ea - ger foot - steps hie - ing!
Thus an - gels sang to shep - herds low - ly:

Text Verses 1-3: © Copyright Magdalene College, Cambridge.
Text Verse 4 and Music: © Copyright 1993 by Kevin Mayhew Ltd.
It is illegal to photocopy music.

shep - herds, in flow - 'ry fields in May.
start - ed to climb the morn - ing skies!
Wor - ship the Sa - viour born to - day.
'Good - will be - gin and ne - ver cease.'

Whence is that good - ly fra - grance flow - ing,
What is that light so bril - liant, break - ing
Beth - le - hem! There in man - ger ly - ing,
'All glo - ry be to God most ho - ly,

steal - ing our sen - ses all a - way?
here in the night a - cross our eyes?
find your Re - deem - er, haste a - way.
and on the earth let there be peace.'

Text: Translated from the French by Allen Beville Ramsay (1872-1955) and Neil Jenkins
Music: French Noël (Beggar's Opera Version) arranged Neil Jenkins

203

93 WHILE SHEPHERDS WATCHED (1)

1. While shep - herds watched their flocks by night, all
2. 'Fear not,' said he, (for migh - ty dread had
3. To you in Da - vid's town this day is
4. The heav'n - ly babe you there shall find to

seat - ed on the ground, the an - gel of the
seized their troub - led mind); 'glad ti - dings of great
born of Da - vid's line a Sa - viour, who is
hu - man view dis - played, all mean - ly wrapped in

Lord came down, and glo - ry shone a - round.
joy I bring to you and all man - kind.
Christ the Lord, and this shall be the sign:
swa - thing bands, and in a man - ger laid.'

5. Thus spake the seraph, and forthwith
appeared a shining throng
of angels praising God, who thus
addressed their joyful song:

6. 'All glory be to God on high,
and to the earth be peace;
good-will henceforth from heaven to men
begin and never cease.'

Text: Nahum Tate (1652-1715)
Music: From Thomas Este's *Psalter* (1592)

94 WHILE SHEPHERDS WATCHED (2)

1. While shepherds watched their flocks by night, all
2. 'Fear not,' said he, (for mighty dread had
3. To you in David's town this day is
4. The heav'nly babe you there shall find to

seated on the ground, the angel of the Lord came down, and
seized their troubled mind); 'glad tidings of great joy I bring to
born of David's line a Saviour, who is Christ the Lord, and
human view displayed, all meanly wrapped in swathing bands, and

glory shone around, and glory shone around.
you and all mankind, to you and all mankind.
this shall be the sign, and this shall be the sign:
in a manger laid, and in a manger laid.'

5. Thus spake the seraph, and forthwith
appeared a shining throng
of angels praising God, who thus
addressed their joyful song,
addressed their joyful song:

6. 'All glory be to God on high,
and to the earth be peace;
good-will henceforth from heaven to men
begin and never cease,
begin and never cease.'

Text: Nahum Tate (1652-1715)
Music: German Melody harmonized by Johann Sebastian Bach (1685-1750)

95 WHILE SHEPHERDS WATCHED (3)

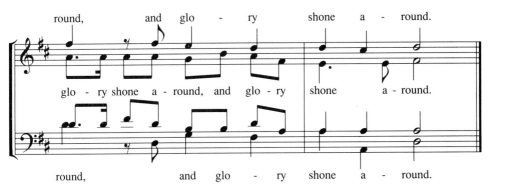

round,   and   glo - ry   shone   a - round.

glo - ry shone a - round, and glo - ry   shone   a - round.

round,   and   glo - ry   shone   a - round.

2. 'Fear not,' said he, (for mighty dread
    had seized their troubled mind);
    'glad tidings of great joy I bring,
    (glad) tidings of great joy I bring
    to you and all mankind.

3. To you in David's town this day
    is born of David's line
    a Saviour, who is Christ the Lord,
    (a) Saviour who is Christ the Lord;
    and this shall be the sign:

4. The heavenly babe you there shall find
    to human view displayed,
    all meanly wrapped in swathing bands,
    (all) meanly wrapped in swathing bands,
    and in a manger laid.'

5. Thus spake the seraph, and forthwith
    appeared a shining throng
    of angels praising God, who thus,
    (of) angels praising God, who thus
    addressed their joyful song:

6. 'All glory be to God on high,
    and to the earth be peace;
    good-will henceforth from heaven to men,
    (good)will henceforth from heaven to men
    begin and never cease.'

Text: Nahum Tate (1652-1715)
Music: Thomas Clark (1775-1859)

Other Seasons

96 KING JESUS HATH A GARDEN

1. King Je - sus hath a gar - den, full of di - vers flow'rs, where I go cul - ling blos - soms fair all times and hours. There naught is heard but Pa - ra - dise bird, harp,
2. The li - ly, white in blos - som there, is Chas - ti - ty: the vi - o - let with sweet per - fume, Hu - mi - li - ty. There
3. The bon - ny dam - ask - rose is known as Pa - ti - ence: the blithe and thrif - ty ma - ri - gold, O - be - di - ence. There

dul - ci - mer, lute, with

4. The crown imperial bloometh too in yonder place;
   'tis Charity, of stock divine, the flower of grace.
   There naught is heard but Paradise bird,
   harp, dulcimer, lute,
   with cymbal, trump and tymbal,
   and the tender, soothing flute.

5. Yet, 'mid the brave, the bravest prize of all may claim
   the star of Bethlem, Jesus, blessèd be his name!
   There naught is heard but Paradise bird,
   harp, dulcimer, lute,
   with cymbal, trump and tymbal,
   and the tender, soothing flute.

6. Ah! Jesu Lord, my heal and weal, my bliss complete,
   make thou my heart thy garden-plot, fair, trim and neat,
   that I may hear this music clear:
   harp, dulcimer, lute,
   with cymbal, trump and tymbal,
   and the tender, soothing flute.

Text: Translated from the Dutch by George Ratcliffe Woodward (1848-1934)
Music: Dutch Melody arranged Charles Wood (1866-1926)

97 THE OLD YEAR NOW AWAY IS FLED (1)

1. The old year now a - way is fled, the
2. The name - day now of Christ we keep, who
3. And now with New Year's gifts each friend un -
4. And now let all the com - pa - ny in

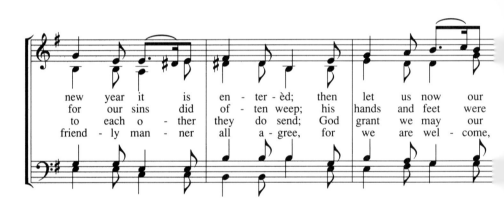

new year it is en - ter - èd; then let us now our
for our sins did of - ten weep; his hands and feet were
to each o - ther they do send; God grant we may our
friend - ly man - ner all a - gree, for we are wel - come,

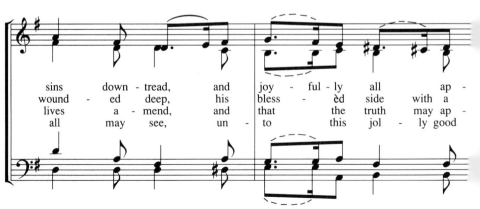

sins down - tread, and joy - ful - ly all ap -
wound - ed deep, his bless - èd side with a
lives a - mend, and that the truth may ap -
all may see, un - to this jol - ly good

pear: | let's | mer - ry be | this | ho - ly day, | and
spear; | his | head they crown - èd | then | with thorn, | and
pear. | Now, | like the snake, | cast | off your skin | of
cheer. | I | thank my mas - ter | and | my dame, | the

let | us now both | sport and play: | hang | sor - row, let's | cast
at | him they did | laugh and scorn | who | for to save | our
e - | vil thoughts and | wick - ed sin, | and | to a - mend | this
which | are foun - ders | of the same; | to | eat and drink | now

care a - way! | God send you a hap - py New | Year!
souls was born: | God send you a hap - py New | Year!
year be - gin: | God send you a hap - py New | Year!
is no shame: | God send you a hap - py New | Year!

Text: A Waits Carol (1642)
Music: Traditional English Melody arranged John Stainer (1840-1901) and adapted Neil Jenkins

98 THE OLD YEAR NOW AWAY IS FLED (2)

1. The old year now away is fled, the
2. Let's mer - ry be this ho - ly day, and
3. And now with New Year's gifts each friend un -
4. Now, like the snake, cast off your skin of

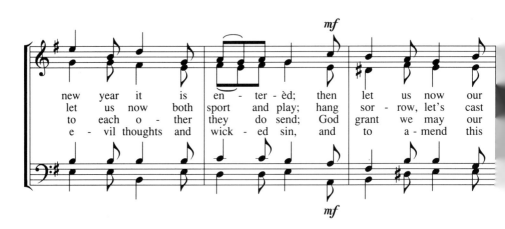

new year it is en - ter - èd; then let us now our
let us now both sport and play; hang sor - row, let's cast
to each o - ther they do send; God grant we may our
e - vil thoughts and wick - ed sin, and to a - mend this

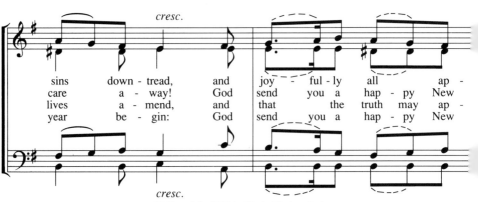

sins down - tread, and joy - ful - ly all ap -
care a - way! God send you a hap - py New
lives a - mend, and that the truth may ap -
year be - gin: God send you a hap - py New

pear,   and   joy - ful - ly   all   ap - pear.
Year,   God   send   you   a   hap - py   New   Year!
pear,   and   that   the   truth   may   ap - pear.
Year,   God   send   you   a   hap - py   New   Year!

Text: A Waits Carol (1642)
Music: Richard Runciman Terry (1865-1938)

99 TOMORROW SHALL BE MY DANCING DAY

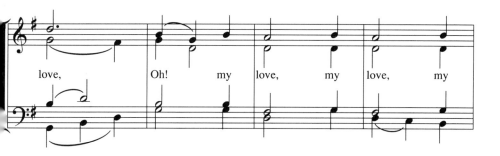

love,   Oh!   my   love,   my   love,   my

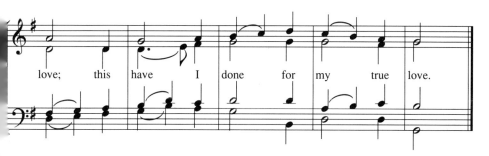

love;   this   have   I   done   for   my   true   love.

4. Then / after / wards bap / tized I was,
   the / Holy / Ghost on / me did / glance,
   my / father's / voice heard / from a / bove,
   to / call my / true love / to my / dance.
   Refrain

5. In / to the / desert / I was / led,
   where / I fast / ed with / out sub / stance;
   the / devil bade / me make / stones my / bread,
   to / have me / break my / true love's / dance.
   Refrain

6. For / thirty pence / Ju / das me / sold,
   his / covetous / ness for / to ad / vance;
   Mark / whom I / kiss, the / same do / hold,
   the / same is / he shall / lead the / dance.
   Refrain

7. Be / fore Pi / late then / I was / brought,
   where / Barabbas / had de / liver / ance,
   they / scourgèd / me and / set me at / nought,
   judged / me to / die to / lead the / dance.
   Refrain

8. Then / on the / cross han / gèd I was,
   where / a spear / to my / heart did / glance,
   there / issued / forth both / water and / blood,
   to / call my / true love / to my dance.
   Refrain

9. Then / down to / hell I / took my / way
   for / my true / love's de / liver / ance,
   and / rose a / gain on / the third / day,
   up / to my / true love / to the / dance.
   Refrain

10. Then / up to / heav'n I / did a / scend,
    where / now I / dwell in / sure sub / stance,
    on / the right / hand of / God, that / man
    may / come un / to the / general / dance.
    Refrain

Text: From William Sandys' *Christmas Carols, Ancient and Modern* (1833)
Music: Traditional English Melody arranged Richard Runciman Terry (1865-1938)

217

100 WHEN JESUS CHRIST WAS YET A CHILD

1. When Je-sus Christ was yet a child he had a gar-den

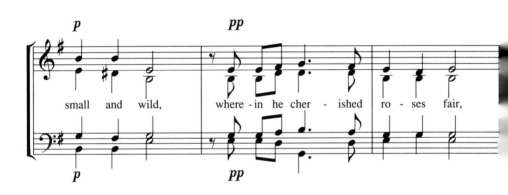

small and wild, where-in he cher-ished ro-ses fair,

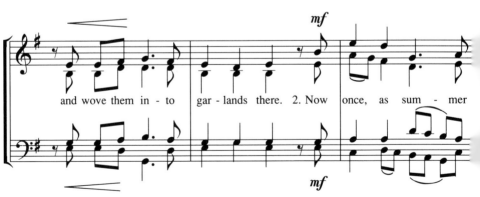

and wove them in-to gar-lands there. 2. Now once, as sum-mer

time drew nigh, there came a troop of chil - dren by,

and see - ing ro - ses on the tree, with shouts they plucked them

mer - ri - ly. 3.'Do you bind ro - ses in your hair?' they

cried, in scorn, to Je - sus there. The boy said hum - bly:

Text: Translated from the Russian by Geoffrey Dearmer
Music: Peter Ilyich Tchaikovsky (1840-1893)

Index